LEGENDS OF GREECE AND ROME

LEGENDS OF GREECE AND ROME

BY

GRACE H. KUPFER M.A.

O, may I join the choir invisible
Of those immortal dead who live again
In minds made better by their presence ; live
In pulses stirred to generosity,
In deeds of daring rectitude, in scorn
Of miserable aims that end with self.
GEORGE ELIOT

HARRAP   LONDON

Published by
GEORGE G. HARRAP & CO. LTD
182-184 High Holborn, London WC1V 7AX

First Edition 1897
Reprinted: 1898 (*twice*); 1899; 1900; 1902
Second Edition Enlarged 1903
Reprinted: 1905; 1906
Third Edition Entirely Reset and Further Enlarged 1907
Reprinted: 1907; 1908 (*twice*); 1909 (*twice*);
1910 (*three times*); 1911 (*twice*); 1912 (*twice*);
1913; 1914; 1915; 1916; 1917; 1918; 1919;
1920; 1922 (*twice*); 1923; 1924; 1925;
1926 (*twice*); 1927 (*twice*); 1928; 1929 (*twice*);
1930; 1932; 1933; 1934; 1936; 1937 (*twice*)
Reset and reprinted 1938
Reprinted: 1938 (*four times*); 1939; 1941; 1943;
1944; 1945; 1947; 1949; 1952; 1953;
1955; 1956; 1957; 1958; 1961; 1963;
1966; 1968
Fourth edition 1972
Reprinted: 1973; 1975; 1978
ISBN 0 245 50856 2

Printed in Great Britain by offset lithography by
Billing & Sons Ltd, Guildford, London and Worcester

PREFACE

ALMOST all boys and girls like fairy tales;
they appeal to the imaginative side of the
child's nature. We cannot make reading
effective as a means of education unless we make
it a pleasure as well: we must recognize the
activity of the imagination in childhood.

Myths are closely akin to fairy tales, and nothing
in the whole field of literature can so well serve our
purpose. The myths of the Greeks and Romans
are especially valuable because they have become
an inseparable part of art and literature. They
have an historical value, too, in conveying to the
reader some idea of the thoughts and habits of the
beauty-loving people with whom they originated.

In this little book I have gathered together
some of the most pleasing of these myths, and
have told them in simple, fairy-tale style, without
any attempt to explain their origin, or to point a
moral. If they please and interest the child, they
will fulfil their purpose.

I have avoided the use of an undue number
of proper names—those stumbling-blocks in the
pathway of a young reader. Just enough have
been given to hold the reader's interest and to

7

make him familiar with the chief characters in the mythical play—characters that he will meet again and again in literature and art. The pronouncing list at the end of the book includes all these names, and with a little help here and there from the teacher they need cause the pupil no difficulty.

Following many of the stories there are poems bearing directly on the subjects. These have been selected with the utmost care. They are designed not merely to introduce the children to some of our greatest authors, but also to cultivate a taste for what is purest and best in literature.

G. H. K.

CONTENTS

9

10 Legends of Greece and Rome

Contents

12   Legends of Greece and Rome

LEGENDS OF GREECE AND ROME

The Kingdom above the Clouds

L ONG, long ago, there lived, in the land which we call Greece, a race of brave men and beautiful women. They thought their own land the best and the fairest in the world; and as they watched the sunsets and the rising of the moon and all the other beautiful things that nature showed them, they were filled with awe and wonder.

So they said, " There must be some mighty people living above us, who rule the sun and the moon and the stars and the oceans and the rivers and the woods and everything else. They are great and happy and good, and they live for ever; they can do whatever they please, and from them come all our joys and sorrows. Let us worship them and sing of them." And they called these mighty people gods and goddesses.

In the northern part of Greece, there stood a lofty mountain called Olympus. Its sides were covered with thick, green woods; and it was so high that its peak seemed to pierce through the clouds, up, up into the sky, till the eye could scarcely follow it. None of the people of Greece had ever climbed to the top of Mount Olympus, and they said it was there that the gods lived, among the clouds and the stars.

They pictured the marble halls, with their great, shining pillars and their thrones of gold and silver. The walls of the palaces, they said, were covered with pictures such as no man's hand had ever painted—pictures such as we sometimes see in the sunset sky, when the pink and gold and purple cloudlets sink into the west, changing their shape each moment that we gaze at them.

Up in the land above the clouds, it was spring-time all the year round. It never rained there, and it was never cold ; the birds sang from morning till night, and the flowers bloomed from one year's end to the other.

Sometimes the mighty rulers of the sun and the moon and all the world left their homes and came down to visit the people on the earth. Once in a great, great while they came in their own true forms ; but far oftener they took on the shape of animals or human beings, so that they might not be recognized.

The people of Greece, who made up all the stories I am going to tell you, believed that if they did anything wrong it would displease the gods, and that they would be punished by sickness or death or some other evil ; but if they did what was right, the mighty people would be pleased and would love them and send them wealth and happiness.

So they built great temples of marble, and in them they set up gold and ivory statues of the gods ; and there they came, in time of trouble, to ask for help and comfort ; and when they were happy they came to offer up their thanks to the kind gods.

The king of the gods was Jupiter, who ruled not only the people of the earth, but the mightier people of the heavens. He it was who hurled the thunderbolts and guided the winds and the waters, and, in a word, ruled over all heaven and earth. His wife was Juno, the queen of heaven, who helped him in his work. I am afraid you will not love Juno very much by the time you have read all the stories I am going to tell you ; for she was selfish and jealous, and, like all such people, often made herself and others very unhappy. She had one great favourite, a peacock, which was always with her.

Besides Jupiter and Juno there were many other gods and goddesses ; and as you are going to read stories about some of them, I will tell you who they were.

Apollo was the god of the sun, of music, and of

love. He was very beautiful, as indeed almost all the gods were ; but he was the fairest of them all. He drove his golden sun chariot through the heavens every day, and on his lyre he played sweet music. He could heal all kinds of wounds, and could shoot wonderfully well with his golden arrows.

His twin sister was Diana, goddess of the moon. She drove her silver car at night when Apollo had gone to rest in the western sky. She was also the goddess of hunting ; and, in the daytime, she wandered through the green woods, with her arrows at her side, while her fleet hounds sped on in front of her, and a train of young girls and wood nymphs followed.

As Apollo was the most beautiful of all the gods, so Venus, the queen of love and beauty, was the fairest of the goddesses. She was supposed to have sprung from the sea one day, in a cloud of spray, and all the beings who dwelt in the sea, the sea nymphs and the sea gods and Neptune himself, rose with songs of gladness to welcome their queen.

She had a little son named Cupid, who also was the god of love ; and he was sometimes called the god of the bow, because he was never seen without his bow and arrows. You will hear later what curious arrows they were. Cupid was always young and rosy and dimpled ; he never grew up as the other god children did.

Neptune, who was Jupiter's brother, was the ruler of all the waters of the earth. The gods of the sea, and the mermaids and the river gods as well, were his subjects. His palace beneath the ocean waves was built of seaweeds and corals and shells.

I must not forget to tell you of Minerva, the goddess of wisdom and of war. The owl was her favourite bird. She spent much of her time in weaving and embroidering, for she was very fond of this pastime.

And then there was Mercury, fleet-footed Mercury. He was called " The Swift," and no wonder ; for he had winged sandals, and could fly faster than the lightest bird. He had a winged cap besides, and a magic staff wreathed with two serpents, with which he could do all sorts of things. He was the messenger of the gods on all their errands between heaven and earth.

Away down in the centre of the earth there was a gloomy kingdom known as Hades or the land of shades ; and the Greeks thought that people who died went down into this dark land. Its ruler was King Pluto. He was very lonely in his sombre palace ; and one time, as you shall hear, he came to earth and stole away the daughter of Ceres to live with him in his underground home.

Ceres was the goddess of the earth, and the people looked to her for bountiful harvests, and for the growth of everything that sprang from the earth.

Lastly there was Pan, the god of the shepherds and of the woods. He was a strange creature, half goat and half man. But he was loved by every one, and especially by the shepherds; for he guarded their flocks from harm, and played his pipes and danced with them in many a frolic.

And if we believe the stories told by the Greeks, in and about the woods and the waters and the fields wandered all the gods I have spoken of. They lived their lives of mingled pleasure and sorrow, just as did the men and women who worshipped them, and pictured them in their palaces of gold and silver and precious stones, up in the land of the clouds and the stars.

THE WONDERFUL WORLD

GREAT, wide, beautiful, wonderful world,
    With the wonderful water round you curled,
And the wonderful grass upon your breast—
World, you are beautifully dressed.

The wonderful air is over me,
And the wonderful wind is shaking the tree ;
It walks on the water, and whirls the mills,
And talks to itself on the tops of the hills.

The Kingdom above the Clouds

You friendly earth, how far do you go,
With the wheat-fields that nod and the rivers that flow,
With cities and gardens, and cliffs and isles,
And people upon you for thousands of miles?

Ah! you are so great, and I am so small,
I tremble to think of you, world, at all.

W. B. RANDS

THE LESSONS OF NATURE

OF this fair volume which we World do name
   If we the sheets and leaves could turn with care,
Of Him who it corrects, and did it frame,
We clear might read the art and wisdom rare :

Find out His power which wildest powers doth tame,
His providence extending everywhere,
His justice which proud rebels doth not spare,
In every page, no period of the same.

But silly we, like foolish children, rest
Well pleased with colour'd vellum, leaves of gold,
Fair dangling ribbands, leaving what is best,
On the great Writer's sense ne'er taking hold ;

Or if by chance we stay our minds on aught,
It is some picture on the margin wrought.

W. DRUMMOND

Two Gifts from the Gods, and what came of them

IN the far-away days, before men had learned many truths which they now know, they believed that for a long time man lived by himself without the companionship of wife or sister; and sometimes, when vexed by their fair companions, or tormented, it may be, by their own selfishness, they would invent stories telling that woman was sent upon earth to bring evil into their lives. Evidently they did not wish to remember the many blessings which they owed to her.

Some of these stories remind us of our first mother, and the one I am going to tell is about a fair woman who, like Eve, brought misfortune to her husband as well as blessings.

But it was not entirely her fault, because she was sent by Jupiter to do this; and his first intention was that she should bring evil only. In the end, as you will hear, she also brought a very precious gift.

Jupiter was very angry with the earth-dwellers.

Another god, in pity of their toilsome lives, had stolen from heaven the sacred fire which had been denied to them, and in jealous wrath Jupiter determined to send another gift to man which should seem to be even more desirable than the first, but which should work him great harm. And the god laughed within himself at the thought of the trick he would play upon puny man.

First he called upon Vulcan to mould from clay a female form which should rival in its perfect beauty the very goddesses themselves. Now Vulcan was the artist-god, and not even the statue which Pygmalion carved and which Venus changed into a living woman was so beautiful as the figure which took shape under his hands. Nor did the other gods and goddesses stand idly by. Each added some grace and some adornment to this masterpiece, until at last the figure of a beauteous maid, most gifted of her kind, full of life and vigour, and in every way fulfilling the command of Jupiter, stood before him.

But Vulcan, though proud of his handiwork, was not yet satisfied. He was a famous worker in metals, and possessed a wonderful forge, upon which he could forge the thunderbolts of Jupiter or any smaller thing, and he resolved to crown the maiden with a gift such as even he had never excelled.

And well did he fulfil his purpose. Upon her

head he placed a golden mitre wrought with such skill that the very figures upon its ornamented border seemed to be alive.

And now, sure that so beautiful a gift could not be refused, Jupiter commanded that the maiden should be called Pandora, and that she should be taken to the palace of Epimetheus.

She was quickly borne to earth by the ever-ready Mercury, and if the gods were delighted with her, much more did Epimetheus receive her with joy. True, he had been warned not to accept a gift from heaven lest he should bring woes upon the earth. But if he remembered this it seemed easier to risk future ills than to resign so much present happiness ; and so he did not hesitate to take Pandora for his bride.

For a long time they lived happily together in their beautiful home in sunny Greece, and it must have seemed to Epimetheus that the woes predicted would not come to pass. Perhaps, even, he laughed at the thought of anything unpleasant coming through his charming wife. But the gods do not forget their purposes. Jupiter had sent another gift to the palace of Pandora's husband in the shape of a finely carved casket, and inscribed on this was a warning that it must not be opened until the gods permitted.

Pandora often felt a great desire to open this casket, but she tried not to yield to the temptation.

She loved her husband dearly, and would not for the world have brought misfortune upon him. However, the purpose of Jupiter was stronger than her will, and so one day her curiosity got the upper hand, and in a weak moment she raised the lid.

Poor Pandora ! The air was immediately filled with strange fluttering shapes, many of which, too well she knew, would carry dark ills abroad and scatter diseases throughout the earth. Full of horror, and very much frightened, Pandora shut down the lid as quickly as she could, but everything had escaped, save the spirit of Hope, which Jupiter, perhaps a little sorry at the last, had willed should remain.

And so to this day, as a poet has sung, " hope springs eternal in the human breast " ; and man strives against evil and misfortune with courage born of the hope which Pandora brought from the gods, and which happily she preserved for her husband and mankind.

The Great Bear and the Little Bear

THIS is a story about a woman whom you will all love. Almost everybody loved Callisto and her little son Arcas ; for she was fair and good, and kind to all who knew her.

She had a very joyous nature, and when she went hunting in the forests with her companions, as she often did, she was always the leader of the merry party. She dearly loved the woods with their gurgling brooks and tuneful birds and bright flowers. She laughed and sang to the beautiful world about her, and in return all nature seemed to smile on her.

I said that *almost* everybody loved Callisto ; for although her little boy and all her companions and even the gods were very fond of her, there was one who did not love her, and that was Juno.

For some reason, Juno could not bear to look at Callisto, and the lovelier and fairer she grew, the more the queen of heaven seemed to hate her. At last, one day when Juno met her in the forest, hunting and singing as she went along, all bitter feelings seemed to rush into her heart at once ;

24

and she hated Callisto so much that she could no longer bear to see her.

So she did a very cruel thing—she raised her hand and spoke a few magic words. In an instant Callisto's slender, white hands had changed into great, hairy paws ; and where but a moment before a fair young woman had stood, there was now only a shaggy, ugly bear.

The poor bear, afraid of herself, and of every sound, rushed through the forest, hiding in caves and behind trees whenever she heard the patter of feet on the ground. For although her body was like a bear's, her thoughts and feelings were still human, and she feared the wild beasts of the woods.

For fifteen long years, poor Callisto lived lonely and sad in the forest. Her joy in nature was all gone. In vain the brooks gurgled as they sped merrily by ; in vain the sun looked down with his cheery smile; in vain the birds sang their happy songs. She cared for none of them, and no longer responded to the beauty that surrounded her.

Nuts and wild honey and berries were her food— the running brooks, her drink. At night she slept in the hollow of a tree or in some dark cavern. Often she heard the voices of her former friends, as they went hunting over the hills ; and then she trembled and crouched behind the trees, for she did not want them to find her.

Many a time her thoughts went back to that day when she had last seen her little son, and she wondered what had become of the boy.

So thrice five summers and winters passed, and, in the meanwhile, Arcas had grown to be a fine, tall youth, who, like his mother, was very fond of hunting. So good a marksman was he that he hardly ever missed his aim, and with his faithful hound, and his sharp hunting-knife, brought many a wild deer to bay.

One day he took his bow and arrows, and started out alone. He had been hunting a long time, when, in following a deer's track, he came suddenly into a little cleared space, and saw, standing within a few feet of him, a great, shaggy bear.

Callisto, for it was she, did not hear the sound of footsteps until it was too late to hide, and then she turned to see who was coming. In an instant, in spite of the many years since she had last seen him, the mother knew her son ; and she gazed with wondering eyes at the child who had grown to be such a tall, fine-looking boy. She longed to speak ; but of course her growling would have frightened Arcas, so she merely kept her eyes fixed on him.

At first Arcas was only startled at coming so suddenly within a few feet of a bear ; but soon he became frightened at the animal's fixed stare. There was such a strange sadness in the eyes that gazed at him that he felt a terror which he could not explain. Scarcely knowing what he did, he raised his bow and aimed an arrow at his mother.

Just at this moment Jupiter appeared, and snatched both bow and arrow from his hands. For Jupiter had always loved Callisto, and he was sorry for the harm his wife had done to one so good and gentle. To make up as far as he could for Juno's cruelty, he changed both mother and son into bright, glowing stars, and put them in the heavens, to shine there for ever—the Great Bear and the Little Bear. There you may see them on any starry night and think of their story.

Juno was very angry when she saw the newly-made stars twinkling in the sky. She had tried to show her hatred towards Callisto by taking away her human form, but now Jupiter had made her and her son far greater than human beings. She went to Neptune, god of the sea, and told him her troubles. She asked him to grant her at least one little favour—never to let the Great Bear or the Little Bear enter his ocean palace.

If some time you watch the stars over the ocean, you will see that as the night passes, they seem to sink lower and lower, and at last to vanish into the sea. That is what Juno meant by speaking of the stars entering Neptune's ocean palace. Neptune promised to do as she wished, and he kept his word, for from that day to this, the Great Bear and the Little Bear have never set.

THE GLADNESS OF NATURE

IS this a time to be cloudy and sad,
　　When our mother Nature laughs around ;
When even the deep blue heavens look glad,
　　And gladness breathes from the blossoming ground ?

There are notes of joy from the hang-bird and wren,
　　And the gossip of swallows through all the sky ;
The ground-squirrel gaily chirps by his den,
　　And the wilding bee hums merrily by.

The clouds are at play in the azure space
　　And their shadows at play on the bright green vale,
And here they stretch to the frolic chase.
　　And there they roll on the easy gale.

There's a dance of leaves in that aspen bower,
　　There's a titter of winds in that beechen tree,
There's a smile on the fruit, and a smile on the flower,
　　And a laugh from the brook that runs to the sea.

And look at the broad-faced sun, how he smiles
　　On the dewy earth that smiles in his ray,
On the leaping waters and gay young isles ;
　　Ay, look, and he'll smile thy gloom away.
　　　　　　　　　　　　　WILLIAM C. BRYANT

A Story of the Springtime

IN the blue Mediterranean Sea, which washes the southern shore of Europe, lies the beautiful island of Sicily. Long, long ago there lived on this island a goddess named Ceres. She had power to make the earth yield plentiful crops of grain, or to leave it barren ; and on her depended the food, and therefore the life, of all the people on the great, wide earth.

Ceres had one fair young daughter, whom she loved very dearly. And no wonder, for Proserpine was the sunniest, happiest girl you could imagine.

Her face was all white and pink, like apple blossoms in spring, and there was just enough blue in her eyes to give you a glimpse of an April morning sky. Her long, golden curls reminded you of the bright sunlight. In fact, there was something so young and fair and tender about the maiden that if you could imagine anything so strange as the whole springtime, with all its loveliness, changed into a human being, you would have looked but an instant at Proserpine and said, " She is the Spring."

Proserpine spent the long, happy days in the fields, helping her mother, or dancing and singing among the flowers, with her young companions.

This is one of the songs she sang while gathering flowers upon the fertile plain :

> Sacred Goddess, Mother Earth.
>   Thou from whose immortal bosom,
> Gods, and men, and beasts have birth,
>   Leaf and blade, and bud and blossom,
> Breathe thine influence most divine
> On thine own child, Proserpine.
>
> If with mists of evening dew
>   Thou dost nourish these young flowers
> Till they grow, in scent and hue,
>   Fairest children of the hours,
> Breathe thine influence most divine
> On thine own child, Proserpine.[1]

Far down under the earth, in the land of the dead, lived dark King Pluto ; and the days were very lonely for him with only shadows to talk to. Often and often he had tried to urge some goddess to come and share his gloomy throne ; but not the richest jewels or wealth could tempt any one of them to leave the bright sunlight above and dwell in the land of shades.

One day Pluto came up to earth and was driving

[1] Shelley.

along in his swift chariot, when, behind some bushes, he heard such merry voices and musical laughter that he drew rein, and stepping down, parted the bushes to see who was on the other side. There he saw Proserpine standing in the centre of a ring of laughing young girls who were pelting her with flowers.

The stern old king felt his heart beat quicker at the sight of all these lovely maidens, and he singled out Proserpine, and said to himself : " She shall be my queen. That fair face can make even dark Hades light and beautiful." But he knew it would be useless to ask the girl for her consent ; so, with a bold stride, he stepped into the midst of the happy circle.

The young girls, frightened at his dark, stern face, fled to right and left. But Pluto grasped Proserpine by the arm and carried her to his chariot, and then the horses fled along the ground, leaving Proserpine's startled companions far behind.

King Pluto knew that he must hasten away with his prize lest Ceres should discover her loss ; and, to keep out of her path, he drove his chariot a roundabout way. He came to a river ; but as he neared its banks, it suddenly began to bubble and swell and rage, so that Pluto did not dare to drive through its waters. To go back another way would mean great loss of time ; so with his sceptre he struck the ground thrice. It opened, and, in an instant, horses, chariot, and all, plunged into the darkness below.

But Proserpine knew that the nymph of the stream had recognized her, and had tried to save her by making the waters of the stream rise. So, just as the ground was closing over her, the girl seized her girdle and threw it far out into the river. She hoped that in some way the girdle might reach Ceres and help her to find her lost daughter.

THE VOICE OF SPRING

I COME, I come! ye have called me long;
   I come o'er the mountains, with light and song.
Ye may trace my step o'er the waking earth
By the winds which tell of the violet's birth,
By the primrose stars in the shadowy grass,
By the green leaves opening as I pass.

I have looked o'er the hills of the stormy North,
And the larch has hung all his tassels forth;
The fisher is out on the sunny sea,
And the reindeer bounds o'er the pastures free,
And the pine has a fringe of softer green,
And the moss looks bright, where my step has been.

From the streams and founts I have loosed the chain;
They are sweeping on to the silvery main,
They are flashing down from the mountain brows,
They are flinging spray o'er the forest boughs,
They are bursting fresh from their sparry caves,
And the earth resounds with the joy of waves.

FELICIA HEMANS

A Story of the Springtime

IN the evening Ceres returned to her home; but her daughter, who usually came running to meet her, was nowhere to be seen. Ceres searched for her in all the rooms, but they were empty. Then she lighted a great torch from the fires of a volcano, and went wandering among the fields, looking for her child. When morning broke, and she had found no trace of Proserpine, her grief was terrible to see.

On that sad day, Ceres began a long, long wandering. Over land and sea she journeyed, bearing in her right hand the torch which had been kindled in the fiery volcano.

All her duties were neglected, and everywhere the crops failed and the ground was barren and dry. Want and famine took the place of wealth and plenty throughout the world. It seemed as though the great earth grieved with the mother for the loss of beautiful Proserpine.

When the starving people came to Ceres and begged her to resume her duties and to be their friend again, Ceres lifted her great eyes, wearied with endless seeking, and answered that until Proserpine was found, she could think only of her child, and could not care for the neglected earth. So all the people cried aloud to Jupiter that he should bring Proserpine back to her mother, for they were sadly in need of great Ceres' help.

At last, after wandering over all the earth in her fruitless search, Ceres returned to Sicily. One day, as she was passing a river, suddenly a little swell of water carried something to her feet. Stooping to see what it was, she picked up the girdle which Proserpine had long ago thrown to the water nymph.

While she was looking at it, with tears in her eyes, she heard a fountain near her bubbling louder and louder, until at last it seemed to speak. And this is what it said :

" I am the nymph of the fountain, and I come from the inmost parts of the earth, O Ceres, great mother ! There I saw your daughter seated on a throne at the dark king's side. But in spite of her splendour, her cheeks were pale and her eyes were heavy with weeping. I can stay no longer now, O Ceres, for I must leap into the sunshine. The bright sky calls me, and I must hasten away."

Then Ceres arose and went to Jupiter and said, " I have found the place where my daughter is hidden. Give her back to me, and the earth shall once more be fruitful, and the people shall have food."

Jupiter was moved, both by the mother's sorrow and by the prayers of the people on earth ; and he said that Proserpine might return to her home if she had tasted no food while in Pluto's kingdom.

So the happy mother hastened down into Hades. But alas ! that very day Proserpine had eaten six pomegranate seeds ; and for every one of those seeds she was doomed each year to spend a month underground.

For six months of the year Ceres is happy with her daughter. At Proserpine's coming, flowers bloom and birds sing and the earth everywhere smiles its welcome to its young queen.

Some people say that Proserpine really is the springtime, and that while she is with us all the earth seems fair and beautiful. But when the time comes for Proserpine to rejoin King Pluto in his dark home underground, Ceres hides herself and grieves through all the weary months until her daughter's return.

Then the earth, too, is sombre and sad. The leaves fall to the ground, as though the trees were weeping for the loss of the fair, young queen ; and the flowers hide underground, until the eager step of the maiden, returning to earth, awakens all nature from its winter sleep.

THE FOUNTAIN

INTO the sunshine,
　　Full of the light,
Leaping and flashing
　　From morn till night !

Into the moonlight,
　　Whiter than snow,
Waving so flower-like
　　When the winds blow

Into the starlight,
　　Rushing in spray,
Happy at midnight,
　　Happy by day !

Ever in motion,
　　Blithesome and cheery,
Still climbing heavenward,
　　Never aweary ;

Glad of all weathers,
　　Still seeming best
Upward or downward,
　　Motion they rest ;

Full of a nature
　　Nothing can tame,
Changed every moment,
　　Ever the same.

Ceaseless aspiring,
Ceaseless content,
Darkness or sunshine
Thy element ;

Glorious fountain !
Let my heart be
Fresh, changeful, constant,
Upward like thee !

J. R. LOWELL

The Childhood of Apollo and Diana

MR FROG, hopping into the water or sitting on a log in the middle of a mud pond, is certainly not a very attractive or lovable creature. But he has his good qualities, nevertheless, and he improves very much on acquaintance.

There was once a poet who went out into the woods to sing among the green trees; and his mind was filled with the story of a beautiful woman and two helpless little children, who had been treated very cruelly. While he was thinking about them, he came suddenly to a muddy brook, and in the middle of it, on a mossy log, sat five or six big, speckled frogs, croaking away with all their might.

Now poets, you must know, love beautiful things, and these frogs were very ugly indeed; besides it was the first time the poet had ever seen such creatures. So he turned away from them in disgust, and went home and wrote his story about the beautiful woman and the two helpless children, and he put something about the frogs into his tale. As he had not liked them at all, he made them seem very bad and ugly ; but that is no reason why we need dislike the little speckled creatures, when we hear them croaking in the marshes.

This is the story of the unhappy mother, and of the men who were changed into frogs because they were so unkind to her:

Long ago there lived in Greece a very beautiful woman, whose name was Latona. It is a soft, pretty name, and will help us to picture her to whom it belonged. She was tall and graceful, and usually wore soft, pearl-coloured robes. Her hair was dark, and her eyes were a deep, clear grey. They were sad eyes, because Latona's life was very unhappy.

Juno hated the grey-eyed woman ; and she treated her so badly, and was so unkind to her, that poor Latona had to flee from place to place, to escape the queen's anger.

One day she came to a stream ; and there lay a little rowboat without any oars ; and the ripples of water made soft music as they plashed against its sides.

The water sounded so quiet and restful, and poor Latona was so tired and discouraged, that she stepped into the boat and pushed it off from the shore. She sat down, her hands folded in her lap, softly crying as she drifted along. Night came, and still the little boat went bravely along through the dark water, and the stars looked down in pity, as though they wished to comfort Latona.

It seemed a long time since she had left the land, although it was only a few hours. Towards morning, she was startled from her sorrow by the grating of the keel on the shore ; and when she looked up, she saw that she had drifted to a little island.

It was a pretty place, covered with trees, and along the shores grew many bright flowers. It all looked so cheerful that Latona took heart again and stepped out of the boat to explore the little kingdom she had found.

Nor was she disappointed. Berries and fruits of all kinds grew there in plenty, and in the very centre of the island was a cave which served well for a house.

Best of all, by the side of the cave, ran a brook of clear, sparkling water. It danced along over the pebbles, and wound its way across the little island, and seemed to sing a song of welcome to Latona. In fact, it was as lovely a home as anyone could wish for.

And here Latona lived for a long, long time. She was very happy, and hoped that Juno would never find her in this hidden corner of the earth. After a while one of the gods, who loved and pitied her, sent two beautiful twin babes to gladden her heart. She never wearied of watching her little boy and girl, as they lay asleep or played with their fingers and toes in true baby fashion. She named the boy Apollo, and the girl Diana.

One sad day, when she was sitting in the sunshine with her children, a black, angry-looking cloud spread over the sky; and when Latona looked up towards it, she saw Juno standing before her. With harsh words, the goddess ordered the poor mother to leave the island at once; and, although it made Latona very sad to go from the home where she had been so happy, she hastened away, for she feared that otherwise Juno might harm her two beautiful babes. So she took a little one in each arm, and again set forth on her wanderings.

She came at length to a desert land, where there was not a blade of grass or a flower to rest her tired eyes. The hot sand burned her feet, and her lips were parched with thirst. The two babes in her arms sometimes seemed to weigh like lead— she was so tired from walking all day long. Yet her cloak was always held so as to shield them, not herself, from the sun. The mother was glad to suffer anything for her children's sake.

She had been walking for days and days, the hot sand burning her tender feet, and her throat dry and parched for lack of water, when suddenly she saw in the distance a clump of trees, and a glimmer of blue water amid the green.

The hope of relief gave her new strength, and she hastened toward the spot. When she came to it, she found a lake of clear, blue water. All about it tall reeds were growing, and some rough peasants were plucking them and binding them in sheaves.

Latona bent and tried to reach the pure water with her lips, for both her arms were burdened with the children. But she started up again when the men, in a very rude and unkind tone, ordered her not to drink.

" What ! " said Latona in surprise, " surely you will not forbid me to drink of this pure water, which the gods have put here for all to enjoy ! I am weary from long wandering over the desert, and my lips are parched with thirst." The water looked so cool and inviting that Latona once more bent to drink of it.

But the men only renewed their rude talk and threatened that, if she did not go away, they would do her some harm. Then Latona began to plead, with tears in her eyes. " Surely, if you have no pity for me," she said, " you cannot be so cruel to these little children who stretch out their arms to you." And, as she put aside her cloak, the little boy and girl really did stretch out their tiny baby fingers, as though to beg these hard-hearted men to be more gentle.

But they were very hard-hearted indeed, and

for answer they began to kick mud and stones into the water, so that in a few moments the clear lake had become a muddy pool, and the water was unfit to drink.

Then Latona became very angry, and raising her eyes to heaven she cried, " If there is anyone to hear me, and any justice among the gods, let these men live for ever in that pool ! "

The gods heard her prayer, and the men were at once changed into frogs ; and to this day they haunt the quiet pools, now sitting on the rocks, now leaping into the water with ugly croaks.

As for Latona, her time of suffering was almost over. The twin babes for whom she had borne so much, grew up to repay her, as well as children ever can repay their parents.

Jupiter, the god who had sent them to Latona in her loneliness, had given them his own godlike nature ; and when next we hear of them Apollo is the great god of the sun and of music, and Diana, his beautiful twin sister, is the goddess of the moon. So much did they honour their mother that her lightest wish was a law to them, and nothing that she asked of them was left un-granted.

THE BROOK

I COME from haunts of coot and hern,
  I make a sudden sally,
And sparkle out among the fern,
  To bicker down a valley.

I chatter over stony ways,
  In little sharps and trebles,
I bubble into eddying bays,
  I babble on the pebbles.

I chatter, chatter, as I flow
  To join the brimming river,
For men may come, and men may go,
  But I go on for ever.

I wind about, and in and out,
  With here a blossom sailing,
And here and there a lusty trout,
  And here and there a grayling.

And here and there a foamy flake
  Upon me, as I travel
With many a silvery waterbreak
  Above the golden gravel.

And draw them all along, and flow
  To join the brimming river,
For men may come, and men may go,
  But I go on for ever.

Apollo and Diana

I steal by lawns and grassy plots,
  I slide by hazel-covers;
I move the sweet forget-me-nots
  That grow for happy lovers.

I slip, I slide, I gloom, I glance,
  Among my skimming swallows;
I make the netted sunbeam dance
  Against my sandy shallows.

And out again I curve and flow
  To join the brimming river,
For men may come, and men may go,
  But I go on for ever.

ALFRED TENNYSON

Echo and Narcissus

THIS is the story of a maiden who came to grief because she talked too much, and because she always wanted to have the last word. You can find out for yourselves whether or not it is true, any day when you walk in the woods or go through a tunnel. In fact, I should not wonder if most of you have already tried giving some call when you are passing under a bridge, in order to hear the queer little spirit that lives in such places, and takes delight in mockingly answering back.

Poor Echo! Now she is nothing but a voice, but there was a time when she danced and sang in the green woods with the other nymphs. She had one great fault, however—she was too talkative; and the worst of it was, she told such interesting stories that her listeners would forget how the time was passing.

Many a time even Juno would come down to earth and listen by the hour to Echo's delightful tales. But one day she found out that Echo amused her in this way only to please Jupiter.

46

For Jupiter sometimes grew tired of Juno, and wished to be alone.

Juno was very angry at Echo ; and she punished her in rather a queer way, by taking from her the power of that tongue with which she had been too ready. Poor Echo found that she could no longer speak ; she could only mimic the last words of others.

Now there was a youth named Narcissus, who was as beautiful as a sunshiny day in spring, and he was brave and manly as well. Every one who saw him loved him ; but he seemed to have no heart, for he loved no one but himself.

One day he was wandering through the forest with some comrades, when he stopped to pluck a wild flower, and lost sight of his friends. He turned to take the path which he thought the right one, and in so doing, passed by the tall oak-tree in which Echo lived.

The moment the girl saw him she fell in love with him ; and she followed him through the woods, longing for the power to speak to him. But alas ! she could not speak.

They went on in this way for some time, Narcissus parting the branches in search of his comrades, and Echo stealing softly behind him, until the boy suddenly saw that he had lost his way and called out, " Is there anyone here ? " Echo, who had stepped behind a tree, quickly answered, " Here ! "

The youth was very much surprised, for he had thought himself alone in the woods. He looked all round, but not seeing anyone to whom the voice could belong, he called, " Come ! " whereupon Echo likewise called, "Come ! "

This was bewildering. He could see no one, and yet every cry of his was answered, and the voice seemed very near. He went on calling and questioning, and each time Echo answered in his own words. She did not dare show herself, for fear that he might be angry, but you see she could not help answering.

At last Narcissus, who was getting very impatient, called, " Let us come together here." Echo answered in a very glad tone, and stepping from behind the tree, ran to meet him.

When she came up to him, she tried to throw her arms round his neck, to tell him her love in that way ; for, you know, the poor girl could not tell it in words. But Narcissus hated to have anyone show him affection ; so he pushed her aside very roughly, and fled from her farther into the woods.

Poor Echo ! His unkind looks had hurt her sadly, and she hid herself in the woods, and mourned and grieved, thinking of the beautiful youth who had treated her so rudely. She suffered very much and wept night and day and could not touch any food ; so that she grew pale and thin and began to waste away to a shadow, as people say, until at last her body vanished altogether, and nothing but her voice remained.

Since that time she lies hidden in the woods, and no one has ever seen so much as a gleam of her white arm in the branches ; but her voice is still heard among the hills, answering to every call.

INVITATION TO ECHO

TWO of us among the daisies
    In the meadow bright and still—
You, alone among the mazes
    Of the dark trees on the hill ;
      O sweet Echo,
      O fleet Echo,
Can we not o'ertake you, following with a will ?
            (Ah, Will !)

'Tis my name, but much I wonder
    That you, in your hiding-place,
On the shady hill or under,
    Things you never knew can trace !
      Declare, mocker,
      O rare mocker,
What my sister's name is, else you're in disgrace !
            (Is Grace !)

What sweet things do you resemble—
    Morning dewdrops, starry gleams,
Flowers that in the light wind tremble,
    Beckonings of the rippled streams ?

O dear playmate ;
Come near, playmate;
Are these fancies true, or naught at all but dreams ?
(But dreams !)

Then come down and let us see you ;
If you cannot come to stay,
Ask the stern old hill to free you
Just for half a holiday.
O glad Echo,
O sad Echo,
To escape your prison can you find no way ?
(No way !)

EDITH M. THOMAS

How Narcissus loved his own Image

NARCISSUS, who was so cold to poor Echo, and indeed to all who loved him, at last fell in love himself, and in a very strange way.

When Narcissus was born, his mother took him to a wise man who could foretell the future, and asked whether her boy would live to manhood. The prophet answered, " If he never recognizes h mself." At the time, no one understood the meaning of the words ; but when you have read this story, I think you will see what the wise man meant.

Narcissus was very fond of hunting, and he often roamed through the woods from morning till night, with only his bow and arrows for companions.

One day he had been tracking the game through the forest for many hours, and at last, worn out with the heat and the exercise, he came to a shady spot in the woods, where, hidden among the low bushes, there was a little spring.

The water was clear as crystal, and Narcissus stooped to drink of it ; but suddenly he paused

in wonder, for reflected in the smooth surface
was the most beautiful face he had ever seen.
He looked at it in ever-growing surprise, and
the more he looked, the fairer did the face seem.
Narcissus at last had fallen in love—but it was
with his own reflection.

He spoke to the beautiful image, and the red
lips in the water parted as though they were
answering him; but no sound could he hear. He
smiled, and the two starry eyes in the pool smiled
back at him. When he beckoned, the loved one
beckoned too; and the nearer he bent to the
water, the nearer to its surface did the beautiful
face rise.

When he tried to touch it, it disappeared from
view. That was because, when the water was
rippled by his touch, the image became blurred.
But when the water was still, the face was again
seen in all its loveliness.

Poor Narcissus! He, with whom so many had
been in love, was at last in love himself, and with
a thing that had no form, or substance—a mere
shadow.

He lost all desire for food or for sleep, and
night and day he lay upon the grass, gazing at his
own image reflected in the water. When Apollo
guided his morning chariot over the hills, the face
in the pool seemed touched with a golden light
that made it more beautiful than ever; and at

night, when Diana drove her silver car through the heavens, the poor boy could scarcely breathe for marvelling at the beauty of his own face.

Slowly he began to pine away. The red left his cheeks and his body grew thinner and thinner, until at last he died.

Echo had seen the poor boy's madness, and although he had treated her so cruelly, she felt only sorrow at his trouble. Whenever Narcissus, in despair, cried out, " Alas ! " or " Woe is me ! " Echo sorrowfully repeated the cry. His last words addressed to the image in the water were, " Oh, youth, beloved in vain, farewell ! " and Echo answered, " Farewell ! "

The nymphs of the rivers and the wood nymphs all mourned for their dead friend. And they prepared the funeral pile, for in those days people used to burn the bodies of the dead.

When all was ready, they went with garlands to carry him to his bier, but the body of the dead youth had vanished. In its stead there stood a beautiful flower, with a bright golden centre and soft, white petals, which nodded to its reflection in the pool. And to this day the lovely flower called the narcissus is found by quiet pools, gazing at its image in the water.

A Web and a Spider

IN an ancient city of Greece there lived a young girl named Arachne, whose parents had once been very poor and humble. Arachne, however, brought wealth and comfort into their little cottage, through her great skill in spinning and embroidering.

Such beautiful things did she fashion with her wool, and so graceful did she look as she worked with her spindle, that great lords and ladies came from every part of the land to see her at her work. Her name was famous throughout Greece, and princes and merchants paid her great prices for her wonderful embroidery.

So, as I said, wealth and comfort took the place of poverty in Arachne's home, and the parents blessed their daughter, and all of them lived very happily. Thus it might have gone on until they died, had not Arachne's head been turned by the praises that were showered upon her from all sides. She became so vain about her work that she could think of nothing but how wonderful she was ; and one day she boasted that, though she was only a humble girl, she was far greater in her skill than the goddess Minerva. Minerva, you remember, was the goddess of wisdom and of war ; but in her spare moments she amused herself by doing just such work as had made Arachne famous,—embroidery in wool, or tapestry, as it was called.

Now there was no fault that displeased the gods more than conceit ; so when Minerva heard of the girl's bold speech, she was much astonished, and thought she would visit Arachne to see what she meant by her boast.

Accordingly, she took on the form of an old, grey-haired woman, and leaning on her staff, as though too feeble to walk erect, she came into the little room where Arachne sat spinning. She joined the circle that surrounded the maiden at her work, and listened to the girl's boastful claim that she could outdo Minerva herself in skill.

Then the old woman spoke. " My daughter," she said, laying her hand on Arachne's shoulder, " listen to the advice of an old woman who has had much experience in life. Be content to reign as queen of your art among women, but do not compare yourself with the gods. Ask pardon for the foolish words you have just spoken. I promise you that Minerva will grant it."

But the young girl only looked cross and ugly, as she answered in a very churlish tone, " You are an old woman and you speak like one. Let

Minerva come and try her skill with mine, and I will prove my words. She is afraid of the test, else why does she not come ? "

Then Minerva dropped her staff and cried, " Lo ! she is come ! " and she took on her true shape and showed herself in all her godlike splendour. The bystanders fell upon the ground and worshipped her. But Arachne, foolish Arachne, held her head high, and did not show the least fear or awe ; on the contrary, she again asked Minerva to enter into a trial of skill.

Without more words, the goddess and the humble girl took their stand, each before an empty loom, and began to work in silence. The group in the back of the room watched, breathless with wonder and awe.

In the centre of Minerva's loom there soon appeared figures telling the story of a famous contest in which the gods had taken part ; and into each of the four corners she wove a picture of the fate that had overtaken daring mortals who had opposed the gods. These were meant as a warning to Arachne.

But Arachne worked on at her loom, with the colour glowing in her cheeks and her breath coming very fast. And such beauty as grew under her skilful fingers ! You could almost see the birds fly and hear the lapping of the waves on the shore, and the clouds seemed floating through real air. But the stories that she pictured were all chosen to show that even the gods could sometimes make mistakes.

When she laid down her spindle, Minerva, in spite of her anger at the girl's boldness, was forced to admit that Arachne had won the contest. But this only made her wrath the greater ; and when Arachne saw the look of anger in Minerva's face, she suddenly felt how foolish and wrong she had been. It was too late now for repentance. The goddess seized the beautiful web, and tore it into shreds. Then she raised her shuttle and struck Arachne three times on the head.

Arachne was too proud to submit to such treatment. She seized a rope which lay near her on the floor, and would have hanged herself, to end her shame and sorrow. But Minerva held her back and cried, " Nay, you shall live, wicked girl ; but henceforth you shall hang from a thread, and all your race shall bear the same punishment forever."

In an instant Arachne's hair fell off, and her face became so small that her body looked very large next to it, thought in reality it, too, had diminished in size. Her fingers were changed into ugly spider's legs, and, hanging from her thread, she spun and spun for ever.

If you can find a dusty old corner in an attic, or if you will look closely along your garden wall, perhaps you will see, if not Arachne herself, at least one of her race, spinning and spinning away at a web, as a punishment for that foolish girl's vanity.

TWIST YE, TWINE YE

TWIST ye, twine ye! even so
    Mingle shades of joy and woe,
Hope and fear and peace and strife,
In the thread of human life.

Passions wild and follies vain,
Pleasures soon exchanged for pain ;
Doubt and jealousy and fear,
In the magic dance appear.

Now they wax and now they dwindle,
Whirling with the whirling spindle.
Twist ye, twine ye! even so,
Mingle human bliss and woe.

Sir Walter Scott.

The Story of the Laurel

ONCE upon a time there was a great, great flood over all the earth. Some wicked people had angered the gods, and Jupiter sent all the waters of the earth and sky to cover the world.

He did not want the waters to dry up until all the people were dead, so he shut fast in their caverns all the winds except the south wind, which was sometimes called the messenger of rain. And Jupiter sent this messenger of his to wander over all the earth.

A mighty figure of ruin he was, as he swept along, emptying the clouds as he passed. His face was covered with a veil like the night, his beard was loaded with showers, and his wings and the folds of his cloak were dripping wet. The gods of the ocean and the river gods all helped him in his work ; till, in a short time, the whole earth was out of sight under a vast sea, and all the wicked people were drowned.

Then Jupiter was sorry to see the earth looking so empty and deserted, so he called home the south wind and set the other winds free. The north wind and the east wind and the gentle west wind swept over the earth until it was again dry and green.   After that Jupiter sent a new race of better men and women to live upon it.

But, strange to say, the water had brought forth many queer new animals ; and among them there was a huge monster, so ugly that I will not even try to tell you what it looked like, and so wicked and cruel that the people for miles round the swampy land where it dwelt lived in constant terror.

No one dared go near the hideous creature, until, one day, the archer Apollo came with his glittering arrows, and slew it, after a fierce battle.   The people were then very happy ; and you may be sure that they made a great ado over Apollo, so that he left the country feeling very proud of himself.

As he was going along, whom should he meet but the little god Cupid, armed with his bow and arrows !   Cupid, you remember, was the young god of love, sometimes called god of the bow ; and I promised to tell you how wonderful his arrows were.

Some of them were sharp-pointed and made of shining gold, and whoever was pierced by one of these at once fell deeply in love.   But the other arrows were blunt and made of dull lead, and, strange to say, they made people hate one another. You will hear, in a moment, what use Cupid made of these curious arrows of his.

When Apollo met Cupid thus armed, he began to taunt him. "What have you to do with the arrow?" he cried, in a boastful tone. "That is my weapon. I have just proved it by slaying the terrible monster. Come, Cupid, give up the bow which rightfully belongs to me."

Now, Cupid was a very quick-tempered little god, and he cried in a passion, "Though your arrow may pierce all other things, my arrow can wound you." Then he flew off in a very bad humour, and tried to think of some way in which he could make Apollo feel which of them was the better marksman.

By-and-by he came to a grove in which a beautiful nymph, Daphne, was wandering. This was just what he wanted. He shot the arrow of lead into her heart, and the girl felt a cold shiver run through her. She looked up to see what had happened, and caught a glimpse of Apollo's golden garments above the tree-tops.

Cupid saw him at the same instant, and, quick as a flash, he planted a golden arrow in Apollo's heart. Then he flew away, satisfied.

The golden arrow did its work only too well. For no sooner had the sun-god caught a glimpse of the beautiful nymph than he fell deeply in love with her; and just as quickly, Daphne had been made to hate Apollo, and she turned to flee from him into the woods.

Apollo followed in hot haste, calling to her not to be afraid and not to run so fast, for fear she might hurt herself on the thorns and brambles ; and at last he cried, " Do not try to run from me. I love you, and will do you no harm. I am the great sun-god Apollo."

But Daphne was only the more terrified at these words, and fled more swiftly, while Apollo still followed. He had almost reached her side, when she stretched out her arms to her father, the god of a river along whose banks she was fleeing. " Oh, father," she cried, " help me ! help me ! Either let the earth open and swallow me, or change this form of mine so that Apollo will not love me."

Hardly had she finished her prayer, when her limbs grew heavy, and a thin bark began to cover her skin. Her hair changed into green leaves, her arms to slender branches, and her feet, which had borne her along so swiftly, were now rooted to the ground. Her father had answered her prayer, and had changed her into a laurel-tree.

When Apollo saw that his beautiful Daphne had become a tree, he wept and threw his arms about the newly-formed bark and said, " Since you cannot be my wife, fair Daphne, at least you shall be my tree, my laurel. Your foliage shall be used to crown the heads of victors, and shall be green alike in summer and in winter." And so it came to pass—the laurel, Apollo's emblem from that day on, became the sign of honour and triumph.

If now you should ever hear the phrase "crowned with laurel," you will know what it means, if only you remember the story of Apollo and Daphne.

CUPID

CUPID once upon a bed
　　Of roses laid his weary head ;
Luckless urchin, not to see
Within the leaves a slumbering bee.

The bee awaked—with anger wild
The bee awaked, and stung the child.
Loud and piteous are his cries ;
To Venus quick he runs, he flies.

"Oh, mother ! I am wounded through—
I die with pain—in sooth I do !
Stung by some little angry thing,
Some serpent on a tiny wing.

"A bee it was—for once, I know,
I heard a rustic call it so."
Thus he spoke, and she the while
Heard him with a soothing smile.

Then said, "My infant, if so much
Thou feel'st the little wild bee's touch,
How must the heart, ah, Cupid, be,
The hapless heart that's stung by thee ? "

THOMAS MOORE

The Story of a Sweet Singer

ONCE there lived in Greece a wonderful musician named Orpheus. When he played his lyre, the trees were so charmed by his music that they followed him as he went along ; and the lifeless rocks became living and trembled at the beauty of his song. And he could so charm people that they would forget all their bad thoughts, and become for a while as lovely as the sounds they heard.

Now Orpheus had a fair young wife, Eurydice ; and much as he loved his music, she was still more dear to him. She was as beautiful as the dewy morning ; and it did not take Orpheus' music to make her good, for she had never had a thought that was not pure and lovely.

One day, Eurydice was walking in the fields with some young girls, gathering flowers as she went along, when suddenly from under a cluster of leaves, a serpent darted out with a loud " hiss," and before Eurydice could step aside, the snake had bitten her in the foot.

The weeping girls carried her home to Orpheus,

who did all in his power to restore his dear wife ; but, after a few hours of suffering, she died.

Orpheus' grief was terrible to see. He took up his beloved lyre, but its charm for him was gone. He drew from it such low, sad strains, that even the rocks and the trees were moved to tears for his sorrow. At last he could bear his loneliness no longer, and he determined to go to the Lower World to seek Eurydice—a thing that few human beings had ever tried to do. Hades, you remember, was the land of the dead, ruled by King Pluto and his young wife Proserpine.

To this gloomy place, the bright, happy Eurydice had been brought by the boatman Charon, whose business it was to take the souls of the dead over the dark River of Death to Hades ; and hither Orpheus went to seek her.

Taking his lyre with him, he went along, full of hope, until he came to the black River of Death. Charon at first refused to carry him across ; but Orpheus played for him so sweetly that the stern boatman was melted to tears, and at last agreed to take the player across the river.

But at the entrance to Hades, there was a fierce, horrible dog, with three enormous heads, three pairs of fiery eyes, and three mouths, bristling with ugly fangs.

When Orpheus came to the gate, the dog began to snarl and show his teeth, as an ugly dog will, and started to spring upon this unbidden visitor to the Lower World. But, quick as a flash, Orpheus seized his lyre and drew from it such beautiful music that the dog crouched down at his feet, and licked the hands he had been ready to bite.

So Orpheus passed through the gateway, and after following many dark and winding passages, came to the throne where the king and queen were seated in state.

Before Pluto could express his wonder at seeing a living being in his underground palace, Orpheus fell on his knees, and, fingering the strings of his lyre, told the sad story of his love and loss in a song so beautiful and touching that both Pluto and Proserpine wept to hear him. When he had finished, Pluto granted his prayer and gave him leave to lead Eurydice back with him to earth.

He made one condition, however—that Orpheus must not look back at his wife until they had passed the bounds of Hades. To this Orpheus gladly agreed, and so, after many kind parting words, he started to return through those gloomy passages, Eurydice silently following.

They had nearly reached the entrance, when Orpheus had a sudden fear that Eurydice might have lagged behind. Before he could think of what he was doing, he turned his head quickly to see whether she was still following. But alas ! he caught only a glimpse of her, as, with her arms stretched towards him and her lips speaking a last farewell, she sank back into that Hades from which his love and his wonderful gift of music had so nearly saved her.

In vain Orpheus tried to get back into Hades ; and after sitting for seven days on the bank of the river, without touching food of any kind or sleeping for an instant, he sadly returned to the green earth.

He went up on a high mountain, and there he lived with only the birds and the trees and the wild animals ; for, since he could not have Eurydice, he cared for no other companions. But the birds and the wild beasts and the flowers loved him dearly, and tried to show their gratitude for the sweet music he made for them. They did, indeed, comfort him, and he lived for a long time in this sorrowful quiet.

So time passed on, until one day, as Orpheus was walking on the mountain, he met a band of dancing women who were singing gay songs as they tripped along. Orpheus, to whom the sight of such careless mirth was very painful, would have turned aside ; but as soon as the women saw his lyre, they came up to him and ordered him, in a rough manner, to play them some gay music.

Now Orpheus as you know could think only of sad things ; Eurydice had gone from him, and he felt that he could not play merry tunes. But when he refused, the women flew into a rage, and fell upon him, and put him to death with stones and arrows. Cruel, mad women they were, and their king afterwards punished them severely for their heartless action.

They cast the singer's body into the weeping river. His last words as he floated down the stream were, " Eurydice ! Eurydice ! " ; and the rocks and the trees echoed back the cry, " Eurydice ! Eurydice ! "

The trees and the rocks and the birds and the flowers mourned the loss of the sweet singer, and the wood nymphs and the water nymphs, who had often listened in rapture to his music, grew pale and thin with grieving over his death.

But Orpheus himself, with a happy heart, crossed the dark River of Death into the realm of Hades. This time Charon gladly ferried him across, and the fierce dog wagged his tail in friendly greeting. At the entrance gate stood Eurydice, waiting to welcome him ; and he rushed forward to meet his dear wife and put his arms about her, happy in the thought that they would never again be parted.

ORPHEUS WITH HIS LUTE

ORPHEUS with his lute made trees,
     And the mountain tops that freeze,
   Bow themselves when he did sing ;
To his music, plants and flowers
Ever sprung, as sun and showers
   There had made a lasting spring.

Everything that heard him play,
Even the billows of the sea,
Hung their heads, and then lay by.
In sweet music is such art ;
Killing care and grief of heart.

WILLIAM SHAKESPEARE

EURYDICE

HE came to call me back from death
    To the bright world above ;
I hear him yet with trembling breath
    Low calling, " Oh, sweet love !
Come back, the earth is just as fair,
The flowers, the open skies are there,
    Come back to life and love ! "

Oh, all my heart went out to him,
    And the sweet air above ;
With happy tears my eyes were dim ;
    I called him, " Oh, sweet love !
I come, for thou art all to me ;
Go forth, and I will follow thee,
    Right back to life and love."

I followed through the cavern black,
    I saw the blue above.
Some terror turned him to look back ;
    I heard him wail, " Oh, love,
What have I done ! what have I done ! "
And then I saw no more the sun,
    And lost were life and love.

FRANCIS W. BOURDILLON

The Queen Huntress and a Bold Hunter

THE story I am going to tell you is of that beautiful maiden Diana, goddess of the moon and of the chase.

Every evening when Apollo, her twin brother, sank from sight in his golden sun chariot, she arose and guided her silver car across the heavens. But when the dawn came, and Apollo began his daily journey round the world, Diana left her silvery chariot in the sky and came down to earth.

Clad in her short hunting-garments, her shining quiver of arrows slung over one shoulder, she spent the day in the green woods, enjoying the pleasures of the chase. She was followed by a train of young girls, who hunted and rested with her. But only the fairest and best maidens were thought worthy of the great honour of hunting with Diana.

When they were tired of the sport, they would seek a shady place where, perhaps, a cool brook sped along over the stones ; and there they would bathe their hot limbs, and drink the cooling water, and lie on the soft grass under the trees. No one ever dared to enter these quiet, hidden groves, for they were sacred to Diana and her nymphs.

Actæon was a youth who also was very fond of hunting. More than all else, he loved to follow the deer ; and he had a fine pack of hounds that never failed to track the game when once they had caught scent of the trail.

One day, Actæon had been out hunting for many hours. He was tired and thirsty, and he looked about for some spot in which to rest. Suddenly he heard the sound of running water, and, eager to quench his thirst, parted the branches and stepped into an open space beyond.

But what did he see ? Lying about on the grass were all the fair huntresses with their queen in their midst. At the moment when Actæon parted the branches, Diana was stepping into the rippling water. At sight of him, she paused, flushed with anger and surprise. " Bold mortal," she cried, " darest thou enter my secret hiding-places ? Never shalt thou go back and say to men that thou has seen Diana at her midday rest."

She thereupon sprinkled a few drops of water in his face, and then something very strange happened. Poor Actæon had been so bewildered, at sight of Diana's beauty and at her anger, that he had stood motionless and silent, rooted to the spot. But now he tried to speak, and found he could not utter a word. The angry goddess had changed his form into that of a deer, the animal which he and his faithful hounds had so often hunted.

In terror and dismay, he looked at his new body, which was so strange and yet so familiar to him. At that moment he heard, in the distance, the baying of his own dogs, coming to join him. Ah ! he must hide from them, for they would not know their master hidden in that body of a stag.

He turned to flee, but it was too late. One of the hounds had caught sight of his antlers and had given the cry ; and the next minute, the whole pack of eager creatures was at his back.

Poor Actæon ! He fled in terror, but although his swift feet carried him along like the wind, his antlers caught in the trees and bushes and held him back. At last, tired out by the struggle, he sank to the ground. An instant later the pack fell upon him, and the young hunter was torn to pieces by his own hounds.

DIANA

QUEEN and huntress, chaste and fair,
　　Now the Sun is laid to sleep ;
Seated in thy silver chair,
　　State in wonted manner keep :
Hesperus entreats thy light,
Goddess excellently bright.

Earth, let not thy curious shade
  Dare itself to interpose;
Cynthia's shining orb was made
  Heaven to clear, when day did close;
Bless us then with wishéd sight,
Goddess excellently bright.

Lay thy bow of pearl apart,
  And thy crystal-shining quiver;
Give unto the flying hart
  Space to breathe, how short soever:
Thou that mak'st a day of night,
Goddess excellently bright.

BEN JONSON.

THE HUNTER'S SONG

HARK, hark! Who calleth the maiden Morn
  From her sleep in the woods and the stubble corn?
    The horn—the horn!
The merry, sweet ring of the hunter's horn.

Now through the copse where the fox is found,
And over the stream, at a mighty bound,
And over the high lands and over the low,
O'er furrows, o'er meadows, the hunters go!
Away! as a hawk flies full at his prey
So flieth the hunter—away, away!

Hark, hark!—What sound on the wind is borne?
'Tis the conquering voice of the hunter's horn:
    The horn—the horn!
The merry, bold voice of the hunter's horn.

Sound, sound the horn! To the hunter good
What's the gully deep or the roaring flood?
Right over he bounds, as the wild stag bounds,
At the heels of his swift, sure, silent hounds.

Hark, hark!—Now home, and dream till morn
Of the bold, sweet sound of the hunter's horn!
The horn—the horn!
Oh, the sound of all sounds is the hunter's horn!

BARRY CORNWALL

The Story of Perseus

THERE was once a princess named Danaë, and she had a little baby boy whom she called Perseus. The little boy's father was far away, and Danaë had no one to take care of her and her child.

One day, some cruel people put Perseus and his mother into a boat, and set them adrift on the great wide sea. They floated about for many days, and Danaë held her little boy close, and sang him sweet lullabies, to keep him from crying at the great waves that every now and then swept over the little boat.

She thought that they both would die ; but somehow the frail little bark did not upset, and one day a large wave carried it upon an island, where it rested on the sloping shore. There some kind people found them, and gave Danaë and her little boy a home. The mother and son lived there for many years, until Perseus was no longer a little baby boy, but a brave, fearless young man.

Now the king of the island was a wicked and cruel man, who for some reason hated Danaë and Perseus, and wished to get rid of them.

So he planned some means of getting Perseus out of the way, for the wicked king knew that if the boy were gone he could easily do what he liked with the mother.

At last he thought of an adventure that would please Perseus, and, at the same time, be so dangerous that the youth, he felt sure, would never come back to his home.

On an island, in the middle of the ocean, on whose shores the fierce waves beat all day long, there lived three terrible sisters known as the Gorgons. They were half women and half dragons. They had beautiful faces, but their bodies were so hideous that one could think of them only as ugly monsters.

Instead of skin, they had large scales; their hands were made of brass; but most horrible of all, in place of hair on their heads, there writhed hundreds and hundreds of poisonous snakes, with open mouths and hissing tongues.

Not very pleasant creatures to meet, you may well say. With one blow of their tails or of their brazen hands, they could have crushed poor Perseus to atoms. But worse than that, worse even than the deadly bite of the snakes, was the power of their fierce eyes; for whoever looked a Gorgon in the face, was immediately turned to stone!

Of the three, the most terrible was Medusa; and the task that the king had thought of giving

Perseus was nothing less than cutting off Medusa's head, snakes, and all.

Since merely looking at the Gorgon would turn Perseus to stone, and he could not very well cut off her head without looking, the king was pretty safe in thinking that Perseus would never return to the island.

So he sent for the boy, and when he stood before him, began to praise his boldness and courage, of which, he said, he had heard so much. Perseus, of course, was flattered by these words of praise, and replied, " Indeed, O King, I think there is no task from which I would shrink in fear."

The king was delighted, and said, " If I thought that, my boy, I would let you undertake a task that I am saving for the bravest man in my kingdom."

" And do you think me worthy of this honour ? " cried Perseus, in great delight.

" You may try it, if you like," answered the king. " It is to bring me the head of Medusa, with its snaky black locks."

Perseus gladly agreed, and left the palace. Oh, how the wicked king chuckled over the success of his plot ! In seeming to do the boy an honour, he thought he was really sending him to his death.

Now after poor Perseus left the palace, he began to think over his promise, and somehow the plan did not seem nearly so pleasant nor so easy as when he was talking with the king. The more he thought of it, the less he liked the idea. In the excitement of the moment, he had promised to do something that would surely cost him his life.

When he had passed the gates of the city, he sat down under a tree by the roadside and began to think very soberly ; but the more he thought, the more hopeless did his task seem.

Perseus was a very brave youth ; but the bravest person in the world would rather be alive than be turned to stone, and the thought of what would probably happen to him made him so sad that he could not keep the tears from his eyes.

Suddenly a voice said, " Perseus, why are you weeping ! " Perseus raised his head in surprise, and saw a mischievous-looking little fellow, with an odd-shaped cap, strange, winged shoes, and a staff, wreathed with serpents, on which he leaned as he spoke. It was no other than the swift-footed god Mercury, but this Perseus did not know.

Still there was something so kind and comforting in the tone in which the queer-looking stranger asked the question, that, almost before he knew it, Perseus was telling him the whole story.

When he had finished, Mercury sat silent for a few moments, lost in deep thought, and then said, " My boy, you have undertaken a dangerous task, yet with my help you may succeed. But first of all, you must promise to do in all things just as I tell you." Perseus promised, and in the next story you will hear whether or not he succeeded.

LULLABY

SWEET and low, sweet and low,
 Wind of the western sea—
Low, low, breathe and blow,
 Wind of the western sea.
Over the rolling waters go,
Come from the dying moon and blow,
 Blow him again to me
While my little one, while my pretty one, sleeps.

Sleep and rest, sleep and rest,
 Father will come to thee soon ;
Rest, rest, on mother's breast,
 Father will come to thee soon :
Father will come to his babe in the nest,
Silver sails all out of the west,
 Under the silver moon.
Sleep, my little one ; sleep, my pretty one, sleep.

ALFRED TENNYSON

How Perseus went in Quest of Medusa's Head

NOW all the gods and goddesses had watched over Perseus ever since his birth, and when Mercury came to them and asked them to help the youth, they readily consented.

Pluto lent him his wonderful helmet, which made the wearer invisible ; Minerva gave her shield which shone like gold, and was so bright that it reflected things as in a mirror ; and Mercury himself gave his sharp, crooked sword and his winged shoes, with which Perseus could fly more swiftly than the fleetest bird.

All that Perseus now had to do was to find out the way to Medusa's island home, and the only people in the whole world who knew where that was were three sisters who lived together in a cave.

They were queer creatures, and the strangest thing about them was that instead of having two eyes each, as you and I have, there was but one eye for all three of them.

They took turns in using that single eye ; so that while one of them had the eye, the other two could see nothing at all ; and while they were passing the eye from one to another, all three sisters were, for the moment, blind.

But such an eye as that one was !—worth much more than any other six eyes put together. With it the sisters could see what was going on in the farthest parts of the earth, and that was how they knew the way to Medusa's home.

To this cave, in which the three sisters lived, Mercury led Perseus, and after giving him some parting advice, hid himself in the grove near by, while Perseus stood just outside the cave, behind a bush, and waited.

By-and-by one of the women, with the wonderful eye in her forehead, came to the door of the cave. As she led her sisters by the hand, she told them of everything that she was seeing with the eye— strange things that were happening in countries far away.

They were interested for a while ; but at length one of them grew impatient and said, " Sister, it is my turn to use the eye now. Give it to me."

And the third sister said quickly, " No, that is not true. It is my turn." And the middle one, who had the eye, cried out, " I pray you, sisters, let me keep the eye a little longer. I think I see some one behind that thick bush."

When Perseus heard these words, he trembled in his winged shoes. However, he need not have been afraid, for the sisters fell to quarrelling about the eye, and at last, the one who had it was forced to take it out of her forehead.

Now, at that instant, all three of the sisters were blind, and Perseus, seeing his chance, darted out and seized the eye. Then began a dreadful hubbub, each one of the three insisting that the other had taken the eye, and I do not know how it all would have ended, had not Perseus spoken.

" My good women," he said, " do not be frightened. The eye is safe. I hold it in my hand this very moment."

With a cry of anger the three sisters darted in the direction from which the voice came. But Perseus was too quick for them. On his winged feet he rose high in the air, and then, from a safe distance, called out, " You shall not have your eye back, my friends, unless you tell me exactly how to find the island on which Medusa lives."

This was a secret with which the sisters would not have parted if they could have helped themselves ; but the loss of their precious eye was a thing too terrible to think of. So after a few minutes, they told Perseus all he wanted to know, and he set their hearts at rest by clapping the eye into the forehead of the sister standing nearest him.

Then he flew back swiftly to the grove where Mercury was waiting, thanked him for all his help, and, after bidding him farewell, started out on his errand.

He flew over many lands and seas, until at last he came to the island where the terrible Gorgons lived. He dared not look down, even for an instant, for fear of being turned to stone. But Minerva's bright shield served as a mirror, and, reflected in it, he saw the three monsters lying fast asleep on the shore beneath him.

He took his sharp, crooked sword, and, fixing his eyes on Medusa's image in the shield, he darted down. With one thrust, he cut off the head of the sleeping Gorgon, and then flew up into the air again, holding the horrid head behind him.

The hissing of the snakes on Medusa's head awakened her two sisters, and they started up to follow Perseus ; but on account of Pluto's helmet they could not see him, and he escaped with the head of snaky-locked Medusa.

Back over land and sea he flew, and he had many strange adventures by the way. When he reached the island where his mother lived, he went straight to their little cottage. He laid aside the shield, the helmet, the sword, and the winged shoes ; and, after wrapping the head of Medusa in a cloth, went to greet his mother.

She was overjoyed to see her son, for she had

long since decided that he must be dead. You
see, it had taken a long, long time to reach the
island where Medusa lived ; for it was so far away
that no one but the three sisters with their wonderful eye could tell how to reach it.

Perseus told his mother all that had happened
to him, and, above all, how he had met fair Andromeda, which is the story I am going to tell you
next. In return, he heard how cruelly the king
had treated Danaë during her son's absence ; and
vowed that he would take revenge.

The next morning he went to the palace. The
king was more surprised than pleased to see
Perseus, for he, too, had thought him dead. " Aha,
Perseus ! " he cried, " so you have come back without doing what you promised to do. Your courage
is not so great as you would have us believe."

" Nay, your majesty," answered Perseus, " I
have slain Medusa, and have brought you back
her head."

" That you must prove by showing us the
head," said the king, with a sneer ; for, of course,
he did not believe Perseus.

" Since your majesty insists, behold the head ! "
Perseus cried ; and drawing it from the bag at his
side, he held it aloft in all its horrid beauty. The
king gazed at it an instant, with the sneer still on
his face, and then sat motionless—turned to stone
in all his royal state.

When the people heard what had happened, there was great rejoicing, for they had all feared and hated the cruel king. Perseus chose a better ruler for them, under whom they lived in peace and happiness.

Perseus knew that he owed his success to the help which Mercury and the other gods had given him, and he never forgot the debt he owed them. The head of Medusa he gave to Minerva. She was much pleased with the gift, and placed it in the centre of her bright shield. From that time on, wherever Minerva was seen in battle, there glistened her shield with the head of Medusa, turning to stone all who gazed at its horrid beauty.

How Perseus won a Wife

THIS is the story of the happy rescue of Andromeda by Perseus, which I promised to tell you next. It all happened after Perseus had slain Medusa, and when he was hurrying back to his island home.

In an island near Greece, there lived a beautiful woman whose name was Cassiopeia. Long after the time I am talking of, she was placed among the stars, and on a starry night anyone will show you Cassiopeia's Chair, brightly shining in the heavens.

But at the time of my story, she still lived on earth, and, as I said, she was very beautiful. She was also very vain of her beauty, and one day boasted that she was fairer than any of the sea nymphs. Now the sea nymphs were very fair indeed, and it angered them when Cassiopeia compared herself with them.

People in those day seem to have had very cruel ways of showing their anger. The nymphs sent a sea serpent to the island where Cassiopeia lived, and he did so much harm that everybody was in despair. At length the people went to their temple to consult the oracle.

This was an old custom among the people of long ago. In many cities there were beautiful temples built to the gods and goddesses; and in these temples dwelt priests who were supposed to be the oracles of the gods—that is, through them the gods spoke to human beings. If anyone was in doubt as to what he should do in time of trouble, or wanted to know something that was to happen in the future, he would go to one of these oracles, and offer up a sacrifice to the god, in return for which the oracle would utter words of warning or of advice.

When the men of this place went to their oracle to inquire why such trouble had come upon them, the answer was, " Because of the vanity of Cassiopeia. If she will give up her daughter Andromeda to the serpent, the sea nymphs will be satisfied, and the sea serpent shall trouble you no longer."

Great was the grief of the people at these words. Andromeda was so gentle and good that everybody loved her. Many thought her even more beautiful than her mother, for whose vanity she was to die.

And Cassiopeia herself ? She would not believe the answer of the oracle. She rushed to the temple, and fell on her knees, and offered to make any sacrifice if the oracle would take back that cruel message—that Andromeda must be given as a peace offering to the sea serpent.

But the oracle repeated only the same heartless answer,—"If you wish your town and all the people to be saved from ruin, you must give up your daughter."

Then Cassiopeia went sadly home and locked herself in her room ; for she could not bear to look her child in the face. Ah, how bitterly she regretted the vanity that had led to all the trouble, and how she hated that beautiful face of hers which had formerly given her so much pleasure !

Meanwhile, the sorrowing people led Andromeda to the seashore, and bound her with chains to an overhanging rock. Then they stood sadly round, waiting for the coming of the monster who was to devour the fairest and best of all their young maidens.

Andromeda herself pretended to be very brave, so as to lessen her poor mother's grief ; but in truth she was much frightened, and she shuddered at the thought of the serpent's cruel jaws.

All were watching anxiously, when, suddenly, something black was seen above the water, afar off,—and they knew that it was the dreaded creature. Nearer and nearer came the serpent, lashing the water with its tail and snorting in a most horrible manner. Now it had almost reached the rock to which Andromeda was chained. The poor girl gave one terrified shriek ; and all the people covered their eyes with their hands, for they could not bear to see what was to happen.

All at once something like a little black cloud came darting through the air, a crooked sword flashed an instant in the light, and then was buried in the monster's back.

Perseus, flying above the spot, had seen, at a glance, the girl bound to the rock and the hideous creature raising itself to attack her. Quick as a flash, he had darted down, and was now fighting a fierce battle with the monster.

The people watched the long combat with eager eyes. When Perseus at last pierced the serpent's heart and the ugly creature floated lifeless on the water, such a shout went up from the shore that the hills round rang with the echo.

Then Perseus unfastened Andromeda's chains and led her to her parents. Such happy tears as the people shed! And such rejoicing and praises of Perseus on all sides!

The hero became Cassiopeia's guest, and, after a few days, when he had seen that the rescued girl was as good and lovable as she was fair, he asked for her hand in marriage. As for Andromeda, she had loved Perseus from the moment she saw his crooked sword flash above the sea serpent's head, and so she gladly consented to be his wife.

The girl's parents now began to prepare for the wedding, and the whole village was invited to be present at the feast. Now there was an old man of whom Andromeda's parents were very much afraid. Some time before, he had asked for their daughter as his wife, and the parents had been afraid to say no.

But the girl hated this old man, and that was another reason why she loved Perseus, who had saved her not only from the sea serpent, but from the man whom she dreaded quite as much.

The wedding day dawned at last, bright and sunny, and with great pomp and rejoicing Perseus and Andromeda were married. The people flocked to the tables that were spread with many good things, and the feast began.

When the merriment was at its height, suddenly the wide doors swung back, and the startled people saw, standing in the opening, an ugly, scowling, little man, holding a sword, and followed by a band of armed soldiers.

There was silence in the room, until at length the old man spoke : " Perseus, I have come to claim my promised bride, Andromeda. Give her to me peaceably, or else I and my soldiers will kill you all."

Andromeda was very much frightened and clung to Perseus in terror. Her husband laid his right hand on a bag which he wore at his side and said, " The one you call your bride, sir, is my wife, and no power of yours can take her from me."

" We shall see," was the old man's answer ; and he started towards Perseus.

But in the middle of the room he came to a sudden stop, and stood there motionless, his sword raised to strike ; for Perseus had lifted the terrible Gorgon's head, and instantly the old man was turned to stone, just as he stood.

When his followers saw what had happened to their master, they turned and fled from the house ; and the merry-making went on as though it had never been interrupted.

After that Perseus took his wife to his island home, and there they spent many happy days together in his mother's little cottage.

The Story of Io

IN a certain part of Greece, there was a beautiful grove, bordered on all sides by denser woods. Through it there flowed a restless river, dashing over rocks and scattering its spray, like fine mist, over all the trees on its banks.

The god of the river had one child, a girl named Io, and there was nothing she liked better than to wander in the grove by the side of her father's stream.

One day, when Jupiter had come down to earth, he met Io in the woods and began to talk to her. And he found her so lovable that he came again and again, and spent many a pleasant hour wandering with her along the banks of the stream. Io did not know who Jupiter was, for he came disguised as a boy; and she thought him only a pleasant companion for her walks.

But Juno hated Io; for, as you remember, I have told you what a jealous queen she was, and she could not bear to have Jupiter care for anyone besides herself. So one day, when he had been away from home for many hours, she suddenly made up her mind to go down to earth and see the maiden of whom he was so fond. Her heart was filled with bitter feelings toward Io, and as she entered the grove, her frown was so dark that it seemed almost to hide the sunlight.

I have told you that the gods knew everything. So, in some way, Jupiter felt Juno's wrath before she came into the grove; and fearing that she might harm his companion, quick as a flash, he changed Io into a white heifer. When Juno came to the side of the river, all that she saw was her husband in his own true form and the white cow nibbling the grass at his side.

But she knew that it was Io, and she went up to her side, and stroked her glossy neck, and then, turning to Jupiter, begged him to give her the cow as a present. What could Jupiter do ? He could not refuse his wife such a trifle, and so he had to say yes, although it was much against his will.

As Juno led Io away, she said to herself, " Now that I have you, I will take good care to keep you." So she set one of her servants, Argus, to watch the cow. And a very good watchman Argus made ; for he had a hundred eyes, and no matter how tired he was, he never closed more than half of them at one time. If you or I had fifty sharp eyes watching us day and night, we should find it hard to do anything they did not see.

Never for a moment was Io left unguarded. At night she was tied to a tree, but during the day she could wander about as she pleased. The poor girl did not quite know what had happened to her. Instead of the food to which she was accustomed, she had to eat leaves and grass ; she slept on the ground, and drank from the running brooks. When she tried to stretch forth her arms to ask pity of Argus, she found, to her surprise, that she had no arms ; and instead of the words she meant to speak, she heard only a strange " moo " which came from her own lips.

She was frightened and hastened to the banks of the river where she had so often walked with her boy companion. When she saw her horns reflected in the clear water, her terror grew still greater. The water nymphs, her former companions, did not recognize her ; and even her father only patted her neck and plucked some fresh grass for her.

But that was too much for the poor girl—not to have her own father know her ! She could not speak to him, but with her foot she traced her story in the sand. When he read the sad tale, her father wept aloud, and, throwing his arms about his daughter's neck, gave way to his grief.

Meanwhile, Argus faithfully kept watch, and saw all that had passed between father and daughter. He now thought it time to separate them, so he led his charge away to a distant pasture, and seated himself on the top of a hill, from which he could see all that happened.

But Jupiter had not forgotten Io, and he wished to help her if he could ; so he called his son Mercury, the messenger of the gods, and ordered him to kill Argus.

Mercury flew swiftly to earth, and there put on the dress of a shepherd boy, using his wonderful wand as a staff. As he went along, he gathered the stray sheep that crossed his path, and when he came near to the hill where Argus was watching, he began to play on a pipe of reeds.

When Argus heard the sweet sounds of the pipe, he was pleased, and called to Mercury, " Hail, stranger ! Come share this stone with me ; here are rich pastures for your flocks, and shade such as shepherds love."

Mercury seated himself on the hillside, and tried to put Argus to sleep by ceaseless talking and playing ; but the watchman never closed more than half his eyes. So they had been sitting for a long time, when at last Argus asked the shepherd where his musical pipe had come from, and then Mercury slowly told him the story :

" Once upon a time, there lived in a forest a nymph called Syrinx. She was graceful and nimble and fleet of foot, and she led the wood gods, or satyrs, as they were called, many a race through the woods.

" Now it happened that Pan, the god of the shepherds and chief of the satyrs, saw her one day, as she was passing through the grove. He came up to speak to her, but she was frightened at his goat's legs and his queer furry ears, and fled from him in terror. He followed, but she ran so swiftly that he could not overtake her.

" At last she came to a stream, and here she prayed for help, to her sisters, the water nymphs. They heard her and drew her down into the stream, and a moment later a clump of reeds grew in the spot where she had vanished. When Pan stretched out his arm towards Syrinx, he found himself grasping, instead, the reeds that grew on the marshy banks. Then he gave a deep sigh, and his breath among the reeds made a soft, murmuring sound, like music. Pan was so charmed by the sweet tone, that he fastened some of the hollow reeds together with wax, and thus made a musical pipe, which he named Syrinx, in memory of the vanished nymph."

When Mercury finished his tale, which he had told at great length and in a sleepy tone, he saw, to his delight, that at last Argus was sound asleep, with all his eyes closed. With his magic wand, he made the slumber sounder, and then cut off the head with its hundred starry eyes.

Juno grieved sadly when she heard of the death of her favourite, and she set his eyes in the tail of her own bird, the peacock, where they shine in splendour to this day. But alas! the queen blamed Io for all her trouble, and, to punish her, sent a large gadfly to torment her. The fly worried the poor cow day and night, and bit her and stung her, until Io was almost beside herself with pain.

She wandered from one country to another trying in vain to rid herself of the fly. At last she came to the land of Egypt. There, tired out with her long travels, she lay down by the side of the river Nile, and tried with groans and pitiful cries to ask relief of the gods.

Jupiter could no longer bear to see her suffering ; so he begged Juno to take pity on Io, and promised never again to speak to the maiden if the queen would set her free. Juno herself was moved with pity, and restored Io to her own shape. The people of the land found her by the side of the river Nile, and thought her so fair and good that they made her their queen.

She lived happily for many years, until she grew old and died. Then the people carved a great statue of the queen, and placed it in their temple ; and they called the statue Isis. Hundreds of years after Io was dead, the people of Egypt still came and laid their flowers and other gifts at the foot of the statue of Isis, to show how much they loved their beautiful queen.

SONG TO PAN

ALL ye woods and trees and bowers,
　　All ye virtues and ye powers
That inhabit in the lakes,
In the pleasant springs or brakes,
　　Move your feet
　　To our sound,
　　Whilst we greet
　　All this ground,
With his honour and his name
That defends our flocks from blame.

He is great and he is just,
He is ever good and must
Thus be honoured. Daffodillies,
Roses, pinks, and lovèd lilies,
　　Let us fling,
　　Whilst we sing,
　　　Ever holy,
　　　Ever holy,
Ever honoured, ever young,
Thus great Pan is ever sung.

BEAUMONT AND FLETCHER

How a Mother's Pride was humbled

THERE was once a great city called Thebes, and the king and queen who ruled it had fourteen children—seven brave, strong sons and as many daughters. The queen, Niobe, had much to make her happy— wealth, power, beautiful things of all kinds ; but her greatest happiness was in her children. How she loved them ! She would play with them, and tell them stories, and dry away their tears with her kisses, and she was with them whenever she could steal away from the many things that kept her busy.

Thebes, you must know, was a very great city indeed, and there were many troublesome questions for the king and queen to decide, if they wished to rule it well. But no matter how perplexed or tired the queen was with these worries of her kingdom, the sound of her children's laughter or the touch of their little hands would drive away all care from her heart, and leave her as happy as though she, too, were a child.

Niobe's people did not love her so much as they feared her; for although she was gentle and tender and loving in her own home, when she went out to walk in the city, dressed in her rich robes, she looked very haughty and proud, and she always wanted every one to bow down to her and say, " How great is Niobe ! "

Now every spring there was a festival held in Thebes, in honour of Latona, the mother of the beautiful twin gods, Apollo and Diana. And one year, when, as usual, the women of the city hastened to the temple, with garlands of flowers to offer to the great mother, Niobe came last of all, dressed in a beautiful gown embroidered with gold. Very tall and proud she looked as she walked along, and, at the gates of the temple, all the women turned and bowed low to their queen.

Niobe raised her hand to command silence, and then said, in a haughty tone, " You women of Thebes, wherefore do you worship Latona, whom you have never seen, when here I stand before you with all my wealth and power ? Am I not far greater than Latona ! I am a queen, and she is but a humble woman. She has only two children, and I have seven times that number, each one of them more lovely than Apollo or Diana, whom you honour.

" I am far greater than Latona ; for if all my wealth and power were taken from me, I should still have my children, seven times the number of hers. And even should fortune take one half of them from me, still would I be greater than Latona. Turn from the altar, women of Thebes, and cast away your wreaths. Me, and me only, should you worship, for I am greater than Latona."

At these words the frightened women cast down their wreaths and went silently from the temple.

It happened that Latona had come to the top of the mountain overlooking the city of Thebes, to see the festival in her honour ; for there had been so much sorrow in her life that she took all the joy that was within her reach. And it was always joy to her to hear the hymns sung in honour of the two great twins and their mother.

She heard the queen's boastful words, and hastened to find Apollo and Diana. She told them that Niobe had dared to compare herself with their mother, that she had called her children greater than the gods, and had boasted that fortune could not harm her.

When Diana and Apollo saw their mother's anger, they tried to quiet her, and promised to punish the queen and to humble her pride. As you remember nothing angered the gods so much as boastfulness and pride. So, veiled in clouds that hid their glory, the twin brother and sister went down to Thebes to avenge the insult to their mother.

The seven princes were in the fields, mounted on their fiery horses, chasing one another round the plain with merry laughter. There Apollo found them and let fly an arrow which pierced the eldest through the heart ; and then he shot another and another, until the seven boys lay lifeless on the plain.

The bad news travelled quickly to the royal palace, and Niobe, almost wild with grief, rushed out, bareheaded, with her daughters close behind her. When she reached the plain, and saw the awful sight, she fell upon the ground with cries of anguish.

But her pride was not yet humbled, for, raising her arms towards heaven, she cried, " You have taken revenge, most cruel Latona, and think you have broken my heart. Yet I am still greater and richer than you, for I have seven children left, and you have only two."

Now Apollo and Diana, on seeing Niobe's terrible grief, felt almost sorry for their deed, and thought she had been punished enough. But when she spoke these words of scorn against their mother, their anger blazed forth afresh, and Diana seized her bow and shot her deadly arrows, one after another.

As Niobe saw her daughters falling about her, she seized the youngest and tried to hide her in her cloak, crying. " Leave me but this one, ye gods, spare me this last and youngest one!" But the fatal arrow had already been loosed, and as the words left the mother's lips, the last of her children fell dead at her feet.

Then the childless, humbled woman sat down upon the plain among her dead, and gazed about her in silent grief. And thus she sat, day after day, and never moved nor spoke. Her grief was hardening her, slowly but surely. The colour left her cheeks, her eyes grew fixed in their look of pain, and at last, through her sorrow, she was changed to marble.

The marble image of grief stood upon the plain for many days; until at last there came a mighty hurricane sweeping across the plain, and it swept away the motionless figure in its course. It carried the image aloft to the top of the high mountain overlooking Thebes, and placed it there among the other rocks.

And to this day, you can see the woman of stone seated on the high mountain top; or at least you can see a rock that looks something like a woman; and in the sightless eyes a little stream has its source and trickles down the mountain side, as though poor Niobe wept on for ever.

CHILDREN

COME to me, O ye children!
    For I hear you at your play,
And the questions that perplexed me
    Have vanished quite away.

Ye open the eastern windows,
    That look towards the sun,
Where thoughts are singing swallows
    And the brooks of morning run.

In your hearts are the birds and the sunshine
    In your thoughts the brooklet's flow,
But in mine is the wind of autumn
    And the first fall of the snow.

Ah! what would the world be to us
    If the children were no more?
We should dread the desert behind us
    Worse than the dark before.

What the leaves are to the forest,
    With light and air for food,
Ere their sweet and tender juices
    Have been hardened into wood—

That to the world are children;
    Through them it feels the glow
Of a brighter and sunnier climate
    Than reaches the trunks below.

A Mother's Pride

Come to me, O ye children!
  And whisper in my ear
What the birds and the winds are singing
  In your sunny atmosphere.

For what are all our contrivings
  And the wisdom of our books,
When compared with your caresses,
  And the gladness of your looks?

Ye are better than all the ballads
  That ever were sung or said;
For ye are living poems,
  And all the rest are dead.
                    HENRY WADSWORTH LONGFELLOW

A Mighty Hero of Olden Times

MANY hundreds of years ago, there was born a little baby who grew up to be the strongest and most wonderful man of his time.

When he was but a few weeks old, Juno, who hated his mother and therefore wished to kill the little boy, sent two huge snakes to strangle him in his cradle.

The nurse screamed when she saw the serpents coiling themselves round the child, and her scream woke the baby, Hercules, from his sleep. Starting up in his cradle, he seized the snakes, one with each hand, and wrung their necks. The astonished nurse could hardly believe what she saw.

You can well understand how such a wonderful baby might grow up into a remarkable man. Hercules was, in fact, the strongest man of whom the world has any record. Nowadays, when we wish to say that anyone is very, very powerful, we call his strength Herculean.

Hercules spent the greater part of his life in doing things to help weaker people. Juno still wanted to show her hatred of him, so she sent him into all sorts of dangers. He had to fight hard battles, and kill fierce monsters, and, in short, risk his life all the time. But he was so brave that he feared nothing, and so strong that he overcame all the dangers Juno placed in his path. When the queen saw this, she hit upon a new plan for making him unhappy—she made him a slave to the king of Argos.

Nothing could have been harder for Hercules to bear than slavery; for he had a restless spirit, which made him chafe night and day under the chains that bound him. The king at last took pity on him, and told him he would set him free if he would perform twelve very difficult tasks. Nothing could have suited Hercules better, for he delighted in danger and deeds of valour.

And that is how the hero came to perform those wonderful deeds known as the twelve great labours of Hercules. It would take too long to tell you much about them, for each is a story in itself. There were monsters and dragons and giants and other horrible creatures to be killed, and fleet horses and fierce animals to be captured, and many bloody battles to be fought, before the brave man could gain his freedom. But at last all the dangers were overcome, and Hercules was set free. He started forth on his wanderings with a light heart.

But he had not gone far, when he came to a country ruled by a king who had a very beautiful daughter, Deïanira, and before many days Hercules had asked her to be his wife. The girl would have said yes gladly, but she knew that her father had half promised her in marriage to a great river god. The king was undecided as to what he should do ; but at length it was agreed that Hercules and the river god should show their strength by wrestling together, and that the victor should marry the king's daughter.

Such a way of settling the dispute may seem very strange to us, but it pleased both the suitors. Hercules felt sure that he would win, because he was so strong ; and the river god felt equally sure that he would be the victor, because he could disguise himself, at any moment, and take on the form of an animal.

So when the time set for the match arrived, both the suitors went with light hearts to the meeting-place. The king gave the signal for the start, and the two mighty ones fell upon each other.

Very soon everybody could see that Hercules was uppermost. Against his mighty strength, the river god was like a child. But just as the hero was clasping his great arms about his rival to throw him down, the river god used his magic power, and, in the form of a serpent, glided from his grasp.

" Aha," laughed Hercules, when he saw what had happened, " you think you will escape me that way ? Why, I slew serpents thrice your size when I was but a baby in the cradle." And he sprang upon the serpent, and in an instant would have wrung its neck, when lo ! it had vanished, and in its stead there stood a fierce-looking bull. The river god had saved himself by again changing his form.

Now followed the fiercest part of the fight. The angry bull dashed at Hercules with terrible force ; but the hero was ready for the attack, and, seizing him by the horns, held him down fast to the ground in spite of his struggles, until all the people cried out that Hercules was the victor.

The river god then appeared in his true shape, and yielded his claim. So Hercules gained the king's fair daughter for his bride.

In that last fierce struggle, one of the bull's horns was broken off. The goddess of plenty, or Fortune, as she is sometimes called, found it lying forgotten on the ground. She was so much pleased with its shape that she filled it with her autumn fruits and flowers and took it for her emblem. And this is the story of the origin of the horn of plenty, which we see at so many of our autumn festivals.

THE STRONG MAN

HOW happy is he born and taught
  That serveth not another's will;
Whose armour is his honest thought
And simple truth his utmost skill !

Whose passions not his masters are,
Whose soul is still prepared for death,
Untied unto the world by care
Of public fame, or private breath;

Who envies none that chance doth raise
Nor vice; who never understood
How deepest wounds are given by praise;
Nor rules of state, but rules of good:

Who hath his life from rumours freed,
Whose conscience is his strong retreat;
Whose state can neither flatterers feed,
Nor ruin make oppressors great.

—This man is freed from servile bands
Of hope to rise, or fear to fall;
Lord of himself, though not of lands;
And having nothing, yet hath all.

                              SIR H. WOTTON

The Story of a Poisoned Shirt

WHEN Hercules and the king's daughter had been married, and the feasting was over, they started together to journey to the hero's native land.

They had gone some distance, when they came to a river that crossed their path. Usually it was hardly more than a little stream, but it was now swollen with the spring rains, and the waters had risen to such a height that Hercules was afraid to trust himself in them with his precious burden.

As he was standing on the bank, in doubt what to do, a strange creature came up to him and offered to carry Deïanira across. It was, in fact, one of the men horses, or centaurs, as they were called, who were like men in the upper parts of their bodies, but like horses in the lower parts; so of course he could cross a stream when it would have been impossible for a man to do so. Hercules accepted the kind offer, and with the maiden on his back, Nessus, for that was the centaur's name, started to wade the stream.

Now the undercurrent was very strong, and Nessus was a long time in working his way to the

opposite shore. Before he reached it, he had
planned to run away with Deïanira, and take her
to his mountain cave, to be his wife. So no sooner
had his hoofs touched dry land than he galloped
away, with the frightened girl clinging to his back,
screaming with all her might.

Hercules, who also was having a hard time
fighting the strong current heard the scream, and
looking up, saw what was happening.

He raised his bow to his shoulder and cried out,
" O false Nessus, you rely on your swift horse's
feet to carry you beyond my reach, but my arrow
is swifter than the fleetest horse." Then, choosing
an arrow, he took careful aim, and the next instant
the centaur fell to the ground, pierced through the
heart.

Nessus gave one cry of pain ; then dipping his
shirt in the blood that flowed from his wound, he
handed it to the maiden, saying, " Take this, fair
bride, and if ever your husband should cease to
love you, send him this garment dipped in the
blood of a dying centaur, and it will bring his love
back to you." Scarcely had he finished speaking
when he fell back—dead.

Now the arrow which killed Nessus was tipped
with poison from a terrible creature that Hercules
had slain long ago ; and so strong was this venom
that in an instant it had affected all the blood in
the centaur's body ; so that the shirt dipped in his

blood was poisoned as much as the arrow with which Hercules had slain him.

Deïanira and Hercules went on their way, and, without further trials, arrived safe in the city of Hercules' birth, where they spent many happy years together. So well did her husband love her, that Deïanira had almost forgotten about the poisoned shirt of Nessus.

But after some time, Hercules began to grow restless. He was tired of that quiet life at home, and he often thought of his earlier adventures, until at last the longing to see other lands and to do other great deeds became too strong for him. So one day he started on his journeys.

His wife missed him very much, but she loved him so well that she had not the heart to call him back, since he seemed to be happier in his wanderings.

Hercules had travelled a great distance, when at last he came to a city by the sea. There he saw the king's daughter, and grew to love her as he had once loved Deïanira. He forgot all about his wife awaiting him at home, and day after day he lingered in the palace of the princess.

Of course, Deïanira soon heard how Hercules had forgotten her, and she grieved and grieved over it, till she grew pale and thin. Then, at last, she remembered the words of the dying centaur.

She sent for her most faithful servant, and

giving him the shirt, told him to take it to his master Hercules, in that far-off city by the sea, and to say that she sent him her love and asked him to wear the shirt for her sake. Little did the poor woman know what she was doing, and little did the innocent servant dream of the fate that was in store for him.

He travelled many miles, and at last came to the city where his master was living. He sought him out and gave him the shirt, with Deïanira's message; and Hercules straightway put it on.

In a short time, the deadly poison began its work, and Hercules was racked with strange pains. In his agony, he tried to tear off the fatal shirt, but it stuck fast to his skin. Then the great hero began to stride up and down the seashore, crying aloud in his torture. The servant stood amazed for a moment, and then hid himself, in terror, behind a rock.

Suddenly Hercules spied him crouching behind the rock; he strode up to him, and before the servant could stammer out a word to show his innocence, Hercules seized him, and flung him far out into the sea.

The gods took pity on him, and, as he was falling, changed him into a rock resembling a man in form; and the rock still stands far out in the middle of the sea.

As for Hercules, when he found that he could

not free himself from his torture, he died as he had lived—like a hero. With his own hands he tore up great trees and bushes, and built of them his own funeral pile; then, lying down on it, he wrapped his poisoned shirt about him, and, ordering a friend to set fire to the mighty pile, calmly awaited his death.

The flames leaped and roared and mounted ever higher and higher, as though eager to devour so great a hero; they had almost reached his head, when suddenly the heavens opened, and Jupiter's mighty arm, thrust down from the sky, snatched Hercules away from the creeping, leaping flame. The mortal part of him had been burned away by the fire, and from that time, so the story goes, Hercules became one of the mighty company of gods in high Olympus.

The Artisan's Wonderful Wings

IN ancient Athens, there once lived a man named Dædalus, who was highly honoured by all the people of the city. He made beautiful statues and carvings of all kinds, and he was, besides, a most skilful builder. The most wonderful thing that he had ever built was a strange winding path, called the labyrinth.

Not very far from Greece was the island of Crete, ruled by King Minos, a man who could be a very good friend and a very cruel enemy, as Dædalus soon learned.

Minos owned a hideous monster, known as the Minotaur, so terrible that no words can describe it. The king wished to imprison it in a safe place, and it was for this creature that Dædalus had built the labyrinth. The Minotaur lived in a broad, open space in the centre of the maze, which was reached by a winding pathway—a path with so many turns and twists that one who entered it could never find his way out again.

Perhaps, in another story, you will hear something more about this labyrinth and the Minotaur who lived in it.

But now let us go back to Athens for a while. Dædalus had a nephew named Perdix, a very able young boy, who was anxious to learn to do those things which had made his uncle famous. Dædalus became the boy's teacher. He taught him all he knew and was pleased to find such an apt pupil; but his pleasure changed to jealousy and anger when the boy gave signs of becoming greater than his master. Young as he was, he had already invented the saw and the compass. Athens rang with praises of the clever lad, and it was said that he would some day be far greater than his uncle.

Thus all the uncle's love for his nephew was turned to hatred, and he was anxious to get rid of the boy who was so much in his way. One evening towards sunset, teacher and pupil were walking together at the side of some cliffs that overhung the sea. The boy, not noticing his uncle's gloomy face, was talking happily about all the great things he meant to do by-and-by, when suddenly Dædalus grasped his arm and pushed him over the edge of the cliff into the sea below.

Perdix would surely have been drowned, had he not been rescued by Minerva, the goddess of wisdom, who loved him because he was so skilful. She changed him into a partridge, and he flew off across the waters.

Dædalus soon became afraid of what the people

of Athens might do if they learned of his crime.
So taking with him his young son, Icarus, he
left Athens in the night and fled to the island of
Crete, where King Minos received him very
kindly.

But before long, Dædalus got himself into
trouble by interfering with the king's household,
and Minos made both father and son prisoners on
the island. Dædalus grew very weary of that
life, and thought and thought of some means of
escaping from the island ; but he could not get
a boat, though day after day he looked at the
white-sailed vessels on the water, and longed to
have one of them for his own.

One day Icarus was looking now up into the sky
where many birds were flying to and fro, and then
down at the sea which was covered with sailing
boats, when suddenly he said, " Oh, father, the
vessels look like great, white-winged birds
skimming lightly over the waves. They seem to
fly just as their sister birds in the sky do."

The child's words gave the father a sudden
happy thought. He would try to make wings for
himself and his son, and fly from this island in
which he had so long been an unwilling prisoner.

The same evening, he set to work to make two
pairs of wings. He joined feathers of different
lengths, and, with his deft fingers, shaped them
like birds' wings. When they were finished he

fastened them with soft wax to his son's shoulders and to his own.

Then, with a trembling voice, he said, " Icarus, my boy, watch me all the time, and follow where I lead ; for if you go too low the water may clog your wings, and if you fly too high the heat of the sun will scorch them." He kissed his beloved child, and praying that no accident should befall him, gave the signal to start.

Slowly, like two great birds, father and son rose into the air. The fishermen and the sailors, who saw them passing overhead, thought they must be gods flying near to earth, and fell on their knees. Over sea and land they went, swiftly and steadily, the father ever turning to see that his son was following in safety.

For a while Icarus followed where Dædalus led the way. But after a time he began to feel bold ; and when his father was not looking, flew higher and higher, trying to reach the sky which looked so blue above him.

But alas ! The higher he flew, the more fiercely the sun beat down upon him. Before long the great heat melted the wax by which the wings were fastened, and they dropped from his shoulders. Poor Icarus now had nothing to hold him up in the air, and he began to fall down, down, down. In his fright he cried aloud to his father. Dædallus turned just in time to see his son's head sink below the waves, while the fatal wings floated on the surface.

The poor father flew towards the spot where he had seen his son sink, lifted the lifeless body, and swam with it to the shore of the nearest island. There, with a heavy heart, he dug a grave and buried Icarus.

While he was thus engaged, he heard a strange cry overhead, and looking up, saw a partridge wheeling its flight above him. Immediately he thought of Perdix, whom he had so cruelly killed, and he felt that the death of his own son was his punishment for that wicked deed.

For a long time after that the place was known as the island of Icarus, and the sea in which the boy was drowned was called the Icarian Sea.

BIRDS IN SUMMER

HOW pleasant the life of a bird must be,
Flitting about in each leafy tree ;
In the leafy trees, so broad and tall,
Like a green and beautiful palace hall,
With its airy chambers, light and boon,
That open to sun and stars and moon ;
That open to the bright, blue sky,
And the frolicsome winds as they wander by !

They have left their nests on the forest bough ;
Those homes of delight they need not now ;

And the young and the old they wander out,
And traverse their green world round about ;
And hark ! at the top of this leafy hall,
How, one to the other in love they call :
" Come up, come up ! " they seem to say,
" Where the topmost twigs in the breezes sway !

" Come up ! come up ! for the world is fair,
Where the merry leaves dance in the summer air."
And the birds below give back the cry,
" We come, we come to the branches high ! "
How pleasant the lives of the birds must be,
Living in love in a leafy tree ;
And away through the air what joy to go,
And to look on the green, bright earth below !

How pleasant the life of a bird must be,
Skimming about on the breezy sea,
Cresting the billows like silvery foam,
Then wheeling away to its cliff-built home !
What joy it must be to sail, upborne
By a strong, free wing, through the rosy morn !
To meet the young sun, face to face,
And pierce like a shaft the boundless space,

To pass through the bowers of the silver cloud,
To sing in the thunder halls aloud,
To spread out the wings for a wild, free flight
With the upper cloud winds—oh, what delight !
Oh, what would I give, like a bird, to go
Right on through the arch of the sunlit bow,
And see how the water drops are kissed
Into green and yellow and amethyst !

How pleasant the life of a bird must be,
Wherever it listeth there to flee :

To go, when a joyful fancy calls,
Dashing adown, 'mong the waterfalls;
Then to wheel about, with its mate at play,
Above and below, and among the spray,
Hither and thither, with screams as wild
As the laughing mirth of a rosy child!

What joy it must be, like a living breeze,
To flutter about 'mid the flowering trees;
Lightly to soar, and to see beneath
The wastes of the blossoming purple heath,
And the yellow furze, like fields of gold,
That gladdened some fairy region old!
On the mountain tops, on the billowy sea,
On the leafy stems of the forest tree,
How pleasant the life of a bird must be!

MARY HOWITT

A Cruel King

WHEN Ægeus, king of the famous old city of Athens, was still a young man, he was one day passing through a village, where he saw a beautiful maiden with whom he fell in love. Soon afterwards he married her, and they had one child, a boy, whom they called Theseus.

When this baby was a few months old, Ægeus had to go back to Athens; but, before leaving, he buried in the ground his sword and sandals, and covered them with a heavy stone. Then, turning to his wife, he said, " When our boy is old and strong enough to lift that stone, let him take the sword and sandals and follow me to Athens, where I will make him heir to my throne." Then, kissing his wife and baby, he started on his journey.

Now about the same time that Theseus was born, Minos, king of the island of Crete, also became the father of a baby boy. Minos loved his child very much and watched over him with great care, and the boy was taught all the arts which at that time were thought fitting for a prince.

Every year the people of Athens had a festival, in which all the young men of Greece and the neighbouring islands met to try their skill in various games. When the prince of Crete had grown up, his father told him he might take part in the festival, and so he went to Athens.

Before long almost every one in Athens grew to like him, for he was a frank, generous youth, and most skilful in all the games in which he took part. Only Ægeus, the king of Athens, did not care for him. He was jealous of this young stranger; and one night as the boy was travelling back to the island of Crete, he sent some men after him to kill him on the road.

Perhaps the people of Athens might have blamed their king severely for this cruel act, had not something happened which made them forget all about the young prince of Crete. And this was nothing less than the coming of their own prince to his father's kingdom.

The boy, Theseus, whom the king had last seen as a baby, had grown to be a strong youth, and one day his mother took him to the place where the sword and sandals were buried, and told him of his father's message. "Try, my son," she said, when she had finished, "and see whether you can lift the stone." Theseus bent his knee and, using all his strength, easily raised the heavy stone and took from under it the sword and the sandals.

Then, bidding his mother farewell, he started for Athens.

The journey to Athens was very dangerous, for bold robbers lay hidden behind every turn in the road; cruel giants set all kinds of traps for unwary travellers; and the forests on either side of the highway were filled with fierce monsters. But Theseus killed all the robbers; by his cunning outwitted the cruel giants; and with his father's sharp sword slew all the wild beasts that attacked him.

At last, weary and footsore, yet looking like a king's son, every inch of him, he came to the gates of his father's palace. Ægeus was overjoyed at having such a beautiful, brave youth for his son. He threw open the gates of the palace to all the people, and the city was filled with feasting and rejoicing at the coming of the heir to the throne of Athens. And that was the reason why no one asked after the other young prince.

While Athens was almost beside itself with joy, King Minos, in Crete, waited day after day for the return of *his* son. But alas! cruelly slain, he lay dead in a wood outside of Athens. At last some travellers found him, and brought his body back to the waiting father. When King Minos saw his murdered son, and heard the story of his death, he wept for many a day, and vowed that he would take vengeance on the cruel king of Athens.

And one day, as Ægeus was walking in the palace gardens with Theseus, a messenger came running in hot haste, to tell the news that King Minos was coming against Athens with a mighty army, to avenge the death of his son.

So all of a sudden the feasting in merry Athens came to an end, and all was hurry and confusion as the people hastily prepared for war.

RISE! FOR THE DAY IS PASSING

RISE! for the day is passing,
　And you lie dreaming on ;
The others have buckled their armour
　And forth to the fight are gone.
A place in the ranks awaits you,
　Each man has some part to play ;
The past and the future are nothing
　In the face of the stern to-day.

Rise! from your dreams of the future,
　Of gaining some hard-fought field,
Of storming some airy fortress,
　Or bidding some giant yield.
Your future has deeds of glory,
　Of honour (God grant it may !),
But your arm will never be stronger,
　Or the need so great as to-day.

A Cruel King

Rise ! for the day is passing ;
  The sound that you scarcely hear
Is the enemy marching to battle—
  Arise ! for the foe is here !
Stay not to sharpen your weapons,
  Or the hour will strike at last
When, from dreams of a coming battle,
  You may wake to find it past.

ADELAIDE ANNE PROCTER

A Lock of Purple Hair and
what came of it

KING MINOS, filled with angry, bitter feelings, started to march against Athens with a great army. On his way he had to pass through a large city in order to reach the bay that lay on the other side of it ; but, when he came to the gates, he found them locked, and the people within refused to let him go through the town.

So the army put up their tents outside the gates, and prepared to lay siege to the city.

Now, the king of the city was an old, white-haired man, but, strange to say, hanging right over the middle of his forehead, was a long lock of purple-black hair ; and on this lock of hair depended the safety of the city. The people believed that no stranger could enter their gates, unless he could first secure the purple lock.

When the king's daughter heard that the army of Minos had come, she hastened to the top of a high tower in the palace, and looked about her. She saw the army encamped outside the walls, and seated on a white horse, with his purple robe

fluttering in the breeze, was King Minos himself.

Minos was tall and noble in appearance, and no
sooner had the princess seen him than she fell in
love with him.

She longed to see him more closely and to speak
with him, and felt pained at the thought of the
war which made him her enemy. If only she could
fly out of the gates and tell him how much she
cared for him—she would do anything to win his
love.

No sooner had this thought come into her mind
than it was followed by another. " Perhaps if I
opened the gates for him he would love me; but
I will not, for that would mean being a traitor,
not only to my city, but to my own father." The
girl loved her father dearly, for he was very kind
to her and would do anything to give her pleasure.

Still, day after day, as she watched Minos from
her high tower, the thought of this one deed by
which she might win his love would not leave her
mind. And at last, it no longer seemed so dreadful
a thing.

The end of it was that one night she crept into
the room where her father lay sleeping, and
quickly cut the lock of purple hair from off his
head. She did not even feel ashamed of the
wicked deed, for she could no longer think of
anything but King Minos. Then she slipped out

into the night, unbolted the bars, and, throwing the gates wide open, stood before the astonished king.

" I am the king's daughter," she said, " and for your sake I have stolen my father's purple lock, which will enable you to conquer the city. Take it, with my love."

But Minos stepped back from her in horror. " What ! " he cried, " would you risk the life of your father, and do harm to your city, all for love of a stranger ? She who would do that would do anything wicked. I will have nothing to do with you or your evil deeds."

Morning was breaking as he spoke ; and, waking his men, he marched into the city and conquered it by his own bravery and arms, without so much as looking at the lock of purple hair.

When he had reached the bay at the other end of the town, he ordered his men to seize the ships that were lying there, and to embark without further delay. The princess stood on the shore, weeping, as she watched the soldiers preparing to go.

When at length Minos threw off the last rope, she sprang into the water, and, grasping the helm of the boat, cried, " I will go with you whether you want me or not, for without you life is worthless to me. The gates of my own city are closed against me, for I have betrayed it for your sake.

I will follow you ; for if I have been a traitor to my people, I have at least been a friend to you."

The soldiers pushed her roughly from the boat, and she felt herself sinking, sinking in the waves ; but suddenly her body grew light as air—she had been changed into a bird.

Sorrowfully she flew above the city that had formerly been her home. She longed to speak to the people in the streets, and, above all, to see her dear father ; but the nearest she ever came to his palace, was when she beat her wings against the walls of the tower from which she had first seen King Minos.

The other birds of the air seemed to shun her, as though they knew her story ; so she lived lonely and with no one to love her, as a punishment for her wickedness in cutting off the lock of purple hair.

The Cruel King's Punishment

AFTER a short journey, without further adventures, King Minos reached Athens, and, of course, he found the gates of the city closed and well guarded. So he pitched his tents outside the walls, to wait there until the gates should be opened.

Now Minos had taken along an abundant supply of food for his army, and besides, when that was used up, he could readily send his soldiers for more. But the people in the besieged city had soon eaten up their store of food, and, as you will understand, they had no way of getting any more ; for they could not leave the city without falling into the enemy's hands. Many people starved to death, and all the men were so weak from hunger that they had no strength with which to fight the well-fed soldiers of Crete.

The people consulted their oracle, and were told that they must do whatever King Minos asked, if they wished to save their city from ruin. A messenger was thereupon sent to the king of Crete to ask on what terms he would leave the city.

You remember, I told you in another story, that

whereas Minos could be a very good friend, he could also be a very cruel enemy. What he asked of the people of Athens was very hard indeed; but you must not forget how the poor father's heart was bleeding for his murdered son.

He said that every year the people of Athens must send to Crete seven youths and seven young maidens. These he would give as food to that terrible monster, the Minotaur, which Dædalus had shut up in the centre of the labyrinth.

When the messenger returned and told what terms King Minos had proposed, there was great sorrow in Athens. At first the people felt that it would be impossible to do what the king demanded, but then they remembered the words of their oracle, and said, " Surely it is better that seven youths and seven maidens should die each year, than that every one in Athens should perish."

So all the young boys and girls were called together in the market-place, where they drew lots to decide which should be the victims to the Minotaur. The lots were balls, some white and some black; and the fourteen unlucky ones who drew the black balls went away with King Minos, and were given to the Minotaur for food.

The next year and the next the same dreadful thing was done. Although the Athenians were filled with horror at the cruelty of the demand, they dared not disobey King Minos. But when the time came for paying the fourth tribute, as this sacrifice was called, young Prince Theseus declared that he would go as one of the seven, either to free his city of this terrible yearly burden, or to die with his people.

In vain the old king tried to make him change his mind—the brave prince vowed that he would either free Athens of this unbearable yoke, or else die in the struggle.

THE NOBLE NATURE

IT is not growing like a tree
 In bulk, doth make Man better be ;
Or standing long an oak, three hundred year,
To fall a log at last, dry, bald, and sere ;
  A lily of a day
  Is fairer far in May,
 Although it fall and die that night—
It was the plant and flower of Light.
In small proportions we just beauties see ;
And in short measures life may perfect be.

BEN JONSON

A Thread that saved many Lives

WHEN the day for starting came, the king, weeping bitterly, followed his son down to the black-flagged ship, in which the doomed ones were to sail. How he repented that cruel deed of long ago, in return for which he was now to lose his own son!

Theseus tried to comfort him. "Father," he said, "I am young and strong, and I overcame many monsters and giants even when I was little more than a child. Fear not—I will kill the Minotaur, and come back to you in triumph." And so he went on his way.

During the journey Theseus tried to cheer his companions by hopeful words; but they had no hope, for they thought no human being could overcome that monster, and besides, once in the labyrinth, no one could find the way back to the entrance.

At last the ship reached the island of Crete, and the young people were led into the king's presence. At sight of those comely boys and fair, trembling maidens, any heart might have softened.

But whenever King Minos felt the least pity, he

closed his eyes and seemed to see the body of his murdered boy, and that made him as hard and cruel as ever.

Standing by the king's side was his daughter Ariadne, a beautiful, tender-hearted girl. She wept for pity when she saw the youths and maidens and thought how soon the horrible Minotaur would make a meal of them.

Suddenly the king beheld Theseus, and his eyes sparkled, as he said, " Is not the young prince of Athens standing among you ? " " I am he, your Majesty," answered Theseus proudly, " and I have a favour to ask of you. I pray you, let my companions sleep in the courtyard to-night, and let me enter the labyrinth alone. In the morning the others may follow. "

" The prince wishes to die alone," answered the king. " Let him do so."

All this time Ariadne had been looking with blushing cheeks and a beating heart at the brave young prince. " He shall not die, if I can save him," was her thought.

She asked leave to lead Theseus to the entrance of the labyrinth that night, and when it was dark, she passed with him out of the palace gates.

It was a clear, starry night. A light wind was blowing, and the sails of the boat that had carried Theseus from Athens flapped in the breeze.

When they had reached the entrance, Ariadne

spoke, " Prince Theseus," she said, " my heart grieves for you and your friends who must die this dreadful death. You are brave and strong, and your sword is sharp. Why should you not slay the monster and escape to-night with all your companions ? "

Theseus looked gratefully at the girl who showed such pity for him, and answered, " Fair princess, my arm is strong enough to slay any creature ; but they tell me that even if I kill the Minotaur, I can never find my way back out of the labyrinth."

Then Ariadne gave Theseus a firm thread, and told him to fasten one end of it to the entrance gate, and to keep tight hold of the other with his left hand. If, then, he should kill the monster, he could easily find his way out again by winding up the thread which was fastened to the entrance.

Theseus, after thanking the princess for her help, did as she told him, and entered the gate. Through many dark, winding passages he passed, keeping firm hold of the precious thread ; and at last he came into the open court. There lay the Minotaur, fast asleep, for he expected no food until the next morning.

Stealthily, for fear of waking him from his sleep, Theseus crept up behind him, and with his sharp sword cut off the monster's head. Then he started back, carefully winding up the thread as Ariadne had directed.

It seemed to him that he would never come out of those dark, gloomy passages.   Had the thread broken from its fastening, and had he, after all, lost his way ?   But still he followed it up anxiously, and at last came to the entrance of the cave, and saw the starry heavens once more.   Then he sank to the ground, worn out with his struggle and his wanderings.

Ariadne had been waiting all the while, and she now brought him food to strengthen him, and urged him to flee in the night.   Theseus asked her to go with him and be his wife ; and the girl consented, for she had loved the prince from the moment when first she pitied him and his helpless companions.

Together they went into the courtyard, awoke the sleeping youths and maidens, and led them, wondering, to the ship.

When all were on board, Theseus lifted the anchor, and, rejoicing, they sailed away from the place where they had expected to die.   The Minotaur was dead, and from that time forth, the people of Athens were no longer required to send the tribute to the king of Crete.

How a Wicked City was destroyed

ONCE upon a time there was a town in which the people had grown to be very hard - hearted and wicked. Whenever strangers entered the streets, instead of welcoming them with kind words and offering them a resting-place, these rude people closed their doors against the wanderers, and even pelted them with dirt and stones.

The children would follow them through the streets, jeering and making ugly faces at them, but the grown people were even worse than the children.

Far and wide the place was known for its lack of hospitality. *Hospitality* is a long word, but it has such a beautiful meaning that we can forgive its length. It means those kind feelings of the heart which lead people to give shelter to strangers and homeless wanderers, and to share with them the best fare they have to offer.

In olden times people thought even more of this virtue of hospitality than we do nowadays, and so the conduct of these wicked people was all the more blameable.

On the outskirts of the town, there stood a little, modest-looking cottage, thatched with straw. In it dwelt an old couple, Philemon and his wife Baucis. They were very poor ; but, in spite of their poverty, they were contented and happy, and always glad to share their last crust with anyone who came to their door.

One evening two strangers entered the gates of the city. One was a tall, noble-looking man with massive head and fine features. His companion was much younger, and there was something bright and quick about him. Indeed, at times his feet seemed hardly to touch the ground, as he almost flew along. He wore a curious cap, too, and in his left hand he carried a staff wreathed with two snakes.

The strangers knocked at the door of the first cottage they came to, and asked for a night's shelter. Not only was this refused, but harsh words were given in answer to the simple request.

The strangers went on to the next cottage and the next ; but nowhere did they receive a welcome. Moreover, a crowd of children collected and followed the wanderers with hoots and cries.

Philemon and Baucis, resting in their little cottage after their day's work, heard the noise and uproar and went to the door. When they saw the strangers approaching, with the jeering crowd at their heels, they hastened to meet them.

"Friends," said old Philemon, "our cottage is small and our fare humble, but if you will share it with us, we shall feel honoured."

The strangers gladly accepted, and were soon seated by the hearth, while Philemon heaped on the logs to make the room more cheery, and Baucis prepared the simple meal.

Soon all was ready, and the strangers seated themselves at the table, while the old couple filled their plates. There was only bread and milk, with sweet honey and a few grapes from the vine in the garden ; yet the wanderers seemed to enjoy their meal very much.

As they kept filling and refilling their glasses with the sweet milk, Baucis became worried ; for she knew the pitcher must soon be empty, and there was no more milk in the house. But what was her surprise, when, looking into the pitcher, she saw that it was still full to the brim, and that every time the strangers emptied it, it refilled itself.

Baucis whispered to Philemon what she had seen. Then they watched more closely, and noticed that the honey was far sweeter and yellower than it had been before, and that the poor little grapes from the stunted vine in the garden had changed into great, luscious clusters of purple-black.

Although husband and wife were more than astonished at all they saw, they kept silence about it, quietly waiting on their guests. At last the latter rose from the table, saying they had eaten enough, and would now like a place in which to sleep ; for they had come a great distance that day and were very weary.

Baucis hastened to lead the way to the one bed in the little cottage. When the strangers had gone to rest, she and her husband lay down on the kitchen floor.

Early in the morning, Philemon and Baucis arose, for they wanted to kill their one old goose for the strangers' breakfast. While they were trying to catch it, the two guests appeared in the doorway.

" Come," said the elder, " follow us to the hill-top." And there was something so commanding in his look and tone that the couple followed in awe-struck silence. When they reached the top of the hill, the strangers turned. At sight of the elder man's face, the two simple people trembled, they scarcely knew why.

Then he spoke. " My good people," he said, " know that the two strangers whom you have entertained so graciously and kindly are no less than gods. Look upon your village ! "

Philemon and Baucis looked, and rubbed their eyes, and looked again in wonder. Where but a few moments since had stood a village with its many houses, there was now a lake, sparkling in

the morning sunlight. The wicked people and
their dwellings had all been destroyed.

But most wonderful of all, in place of their own
little cottage, there rose a large, magnificent temple,
with pillars of marble and gold ; and the door of
the temple was of ivory, inlaid with precious
stones.

Jupiter, the god who had worked the wonder,
turned with a smile to the astonished couple.
" My good people," said he, " you alone of all the
village have been saved, and your humble cottage
I have changed into a temple of the gods. Before
I leave this place, ask any favour you choose, and
it shall be granted."

Philemon and Baucis thought but an instant
and then answered with one accord, " Let us, we
pray you, be the guardians of your beautiful
temple as long as we live, and let us die together,
that neither may live to mourn the other."

" Your wish shall be granted," said Jupiter in a
kind voice ; and thereupon he and his companion,
Mercury—whose name I am sure you have all long
since guessed—vanished from sight.

Philemon and Baucis were the faithful guardians
of the temple for many, many years. Whenever
strangers came to the place, they were gladly
welcomed and kindly entertained, for the couple
were just as simple and hospitable in their days
of good fortune, as they had been in their poverty.

So they grew very old—so old that life no longer seemed beautiful to them, and they no longer cared to live. And one evening, as they were standing hand in hand in front of the temple, thinking of the many happy years they had spent within it, suddenly they both vanished ; and in their stead stood two majestic trees, their branches intertwining as though they were whispering loving secrets to each other.

Thus the good people had their wish, both dying at the same instant, and in their stead flourished these two mighty trees, which stood for centuries in front of the temple of Jupiter.

And strangers, who came to the place and heard the beautiful story of Philemon and his wife, would hang garlands of flowers on the branches of the trees, and sit beneath their shade, listening to the wind murmuring among the leaves.

A Dream that came True

I AM going to tell you the sad story of Ceyx and Halcyone, a king and queen who loved each other very dearly.

After they had lived together happily for many years, the king had to journey to a distant country to consult an oracle. He grieved much at the thought of leaving Halcyone for so long a time, and she tried to make him give up the idea of going so far away. She warned him of the terrors of the sea, and the dangers of the storm-beaten waves. But at last, when she found that he was bent on going, she begged him to take her with him. Ceyx would not think of leading Halcyone into such danger, and, although it grieved him to leave her, he felt that he must go ; but he promised to return just as soon as he could.

The ship was fitted out, and all too soon came the day for starting. Hand in hand, husband and wife went down to the place where the boat was moored. There they parted, with many words of tenderness. Through her tears, Halcyone pretended to laugh, and would talk only of the time when the ship would turn its prow homeward.

She stood on the shore, waving her hand, until the boat passed out of sight and only the water, with the dazzling sunlight on it, met her tearful gaze. Then she went sadly back to her palace.

Meanwhile the vessel bearing Ceyx and his sailors sped swiftly along before the wind; the sails flapped merrily, while the happy-hearted crew sang at their work. Ceyx was thinking of his dear wife, and praying that no harm might befall her while he was away.

For a time all went well; but on the fifth day, towards evening, dark clouds gathered in the sky, and a heavy gale arose.

Soon the quiet waves had changed into great, white-capped mountains of water, that dashed and beat restlessly against the frail bark's sides.

Night came on, and the storm grew in fury. The moon and the stars were hidden in dense blackness, broken now and then by a blinding flash of lightning. The roaring of the waves and the rumbling of the thunder filled the air, so that the sailors could no longer hear the orders that Ceyx shouted to them.

Soon the sails flapped helplessly on the broken masts, and the water came pouring into the boat from all sides. At last there came a crash, followed by groans and cries, and the next instant the boat and all the crew sank beneath the raging waters.

Ceyx alone clung to a spar and escaped death

for a time. As he drifted along, now rising on the top of a high wave, now sinking into the foaming depths below, he seemed to see before him, on the water, the face of his beloved wife Halcyone.

At last a large, green wave rose before him, and he had time only to cry, in sad farewell, " Halcyone ! Halcyone ! " before he sank beneath the mass of water.

Meanwhile Halcyone impatiently awaited her husband's return. Every morning, she went to the temple of Juno and prayed that her husband's life might be spared, and that he might soon be restored to her.

At last Juno could no longer bear to hear these prayers for the safety of a man who was already dead. She called her messenger, Iris, and ordered her to go to the home of the god of sleep, and ask him to send Halcyone a dream which would reveal to her that Ceyx was dead.

Iris, in her rainbow-coloured robe, flew swiftly through the air, till she came to the dark cavern of Somnus, the god of sleep.

Into this cavern no ray of sunlight ever pierced ; a dull, heavy darkness surrounded it night and day. No singing of birds or barking of dogs disturbed the perfect quiet of the dark king's home. Before the doors there grew strange plants—poppies and other herbs that send mortals to sleep. In the centre of the cavern, on a great couch of black ebony, lay

Somnus wrapped in slumber. Round him, like vapour, flitted the shadowy forms of dreams and visions.

When the beautiful Iris had entered this dark cave, it shone with a splendour of light and colour such as had never before been known within the place. Awakened by the brightness, Somnus drowsily raised his head, and Iris spoke :

" Sleep, thou gentlest of the gods, who bringest rest and peace to the weary heart and mind, I come from great Juno, who begs thee to send to Halcyone a vision wearing the form of Ceyx, to tell her of his shipwreck."

Then Iris flew back out of the darkness, into the bright, sunlit sky.

Somnus chose from among the visions the gentlest of all, and bade him take the form of Ceyx and visit Halcyone in the night. With swift, noiseless wings he sped through the air till he came to the palace of the queen. He entered, and stood by the side of her bed, wearing the form of her dear husband, his hair wet and dripping, his garments covered with sea weeds and shells.

In a sad voice he told the story of the shipwreck, and ended with these words : " Weep no more for the absent one ; for he is dead, and can never come back to his beloved Halcyone."

Halcyone awoke with a cry. The vision had been so real that she looked for wet footprints on the floor ; but shadows leave no signs, and the room was empty and undisturbed.

She was so troubled by her dream that she could no longer sleep. She arose and dressed, and, as the grey light of morning broke, she hastened down to the shore, to visit again the spot where she and her husband had exchanged their last farewell.

She had been standing there some time, when she saw, far out at sea, something white tossed about by the waves. Nearer and nearer to the shore it came, and with beating heart, scarcely knowing why, Halcyone watched its approach.

At length a large wave came inland, and cast at her feet the body of Ceyx, dead and cold—the hair dripping and covered with weeds and shells, just as she had seen it in her dream the night before.

She fell on her knees beside the body, and weeping, cried, " O my beloved, my dream was but too true ! " She could not bear to think of her lonely life without Ceyx, and she felt that she would rather be with him, even in dark Hades, than live in the bright world without him. So she mounted a little rising knoll near the shore, and sprang into the sea.

But she was not drowned. The gods so pitied the loving couple that they changed them into white halcyon birds, or kingfishers, as they are sometimes called, which live for ever on the sea.

The sailors say that, even in the stormiest seas, there are every year seven calm days, during which the water is as smooth as glass and only the gentlest breezes blow. Then the halcyon birds may be seen floating on the quiet waters. And because of the name of the birds that are supposed to bring them, these seven days are known as the halcyon days.

IN ABSENCE

WATCH her kindly, stars!
From the sweet, protecting skies
Follow her with tender eyes,
Look so lovingly that she
Cannot choose but think of me !
Watch her kindly, stars!

Soothe her sweetly, night !
On her eyes, o'erwearied, press
The tired lids, with light caress ;
Let that shadowy hand of thine
Ever in her dreams seem mine :
Soothe her sweetly, night !

Wake her gently, morn !
Let the notes of early birds
Seem like love's melodious words ;
Every pleasant sound my dear,
When she tires from sleep, should hear !
Wake her gently, morn !

Kiss her softly, winds !
Softly, that she may not miss
Any sweet, accustomed bliss ;
On her lips, her eyes, her face,
Till I come to take your place,
Kiss and kiss her, winds !

PHŒBE CARY

The Story of the Golden Fleece

I. THE FLIGHT ON THE RAM'S BACK

ONCE upon a time there lived in Greece a king who had a beautiful wife named Nephele. Nephele means cloud, and there was something about the fair young queen that made one think of soft, pink and gold-edged clouds on a summer's evening.

The king and queen had two children, Phryxus a boy, and Helle a girl, and they were all as happy as the day is long. Only one thing marred their joy. In the hot summer days, when the sky was cloudless and staring, Nephele would grow thin and pale; then she would leave her home for a long time, and come back only when the soft rain clouds were again in the air.

Indeed, some people said that the clouds were her sisters, and that when they left the sky she had to travel far away with them.

However that was, there came a time when the king began to weary of his wife's long absences. Besides, there lived in the town a beautiful, dark-eyed girl, Ino, who was very much in love with the king. Ino was a witch, who made the king forget all about his wife Nephele, and before long he married the dark-eyed girl.

Now Ino hated Phryxus and Helle because they were not her own children, and because they were beautiful and good. Soon she began to ill-treat them. They had to lay aside their rich clothes and wear old rags and live with the shepherd's children ; and all day long they guarded the flocks on the hillsides.

Still I do not think that Phryxus and Helle were very unhappy. They loved to frolic in the green fields all day long, and healthy young people do not care much about what they eat or wear. Their only grief was at the loss of their lovely young mother Nephele.

Nephele had now been gone a long, long while. The sky was cloudless day after day. Not a drop of rain fell, the fields became parched and dry, and all the crops withered away. There was not enough food for the people, and everywhere they were dying of hunger.

The king at last sent messengers to an oracle in a distant city, asking what he must do to bring back food and health to his people. The wicked queen Ino saw her chance, and secretly bribed the messengers to pretend that the oracle had said that Phryxus and Helle must be killed.

I am afraid the messengers were not very good

men, since they were willing to help in killing the children for the sake of a little gold.

In due time, they came back to the king with their false report—that the oracle had said that only when Phryxus and Helle were dead would plenty and comfort come back to the land. The king was so bewitched by Ino that he felt no grief at this answer, but ordered that the oracle should be obeyed.

Everything was prepared, and the children were led out, decked with flowers, as the ancients used to deck the young lambs they offered in sacrifice to the gods. As they neared the spot where they were to be put to death, suddenly there came flying from the heavens a golden-fleeced ram, which the gods had sent, in answer to Nephele's earnest prayer, to save the children ; for, although Nephele seemed to be far away, she was really watching over her children in sorrow and love.

Quick as a flash, Phryxus sprang upon the ram's back with Helle behind him, and the next minute they were far beyond the reach of the astonished people below.

Over land and sea flew the golden ram—faster and faster every moment, until Helle became so weary of the dizzy flight, that she dropped from the ram's back, fell into a narrow sea over which they were passing, and was drowned. Since that day this narrow sea has been called the Hellespont.

Phryxus, however, clung to the ram's back, and at last they alighted together in the land of Colchis, far away from the boy's old home. Here Phryxus married the king's daughter. The golden ram, worn out with the long, hard journey over land and sea, soon died ; and Phryxus hung its fleece on a tree in a wood, and set a fierce dragon to guard it.

In time Phryxus died and a new king ruled in Colchis; and the greatest treasure in all the land was the Golden Fleece, which hung in the woods, guarded night and day by the terrible dragon.

CONSTANT LOVE

LOVE is a lock that linketh noble minds,
　　Faith is the key that shuts the spring of love,
Lightness a wrest that wringeth all awry,
Lightness a plague that fancy cannot brook :
Lightness in love so bad and base a thing,
As foul disgrace to greatest states do bring.

ROBERT GREENE

THE CLOUD

I BRING fresh showers for the thirsting flowers
　　From the seas and the streams ;
I bear light shade for the leaves when laid
　　In their noonday dreams.

From my wings are shaken the dews that waken
  The sweet buds, every one,
When rocked to rest on their mother's breast,
  As she dances about the sun.

I wield the flail of the lashing hail,
  And whiten the green plains under;
And then again I dissolve it in rain,
  And laugh as I pass in thunder.

I am the daughter of Earth and Water,
  And the nursling of the Sky;
I pass through the pores of the ocean and shores;
  I change, but I cannot die.

PERCY BYSSHE SHELLEY

The Story of the Golden Fleece

II. THE SAILING OF THE SHIP *ARGO*

LONG after Phryxus had died, there lived in a certain country a king and queen who had but one child, a boy named Jason. The king, Æson, was a rather weak, good-natured man ; and one day Jason's uncle came with a large army, and drove King Æson and his family out of their own kingdom. Then the brother ruled as king, while the rightful king lived far away, poor and unknown.

But in spite of his poverty and friendlessness, King Æson brought up his little son like a prince. At that time the wisest person in the world was a centaur named Chiron, and he might be called only half a person ; for, you remember, the centaurs had bodies like these of horses, and heads and shoulders like men's. Chiron was very wise and very good, and many kings sent their sons to him to be educated.

So little Jason went to the centaur's cave on the mountain top, and spent his youth there learning to hunt and to fish and to use the sword and the javelin, and, what was still better, to be truthful and kind.

But at last Jason grew to be a man, and then Chiron told him that he was the son of King Æson, who had been robbed of his throne ; and that he must go and reclaim his father's kingdom.

When the time for parting came, Chiron went with Jason to the foot of the mountain, and said, " My son, forget not the lessons I have taught you. Always speak and act the truth, and be kind to all who need your help."

So Jason started on his journey. When he had gone some distance, he came to a stream much swollen by the spring rains. On the bank there stood an old woman looking for some means of crossing. Mindful of the centaur's parting words, Jason spoke to her and offered to carry her across. The old woman gladly accepted the offer, and Jason lifted her upon his shoulders and entered the stream. The water dashed against him with great force ; he had to struggle with all his might, and was out of breath when he landed his companion safely on the other shore. But what was Jason's surprise to see, in place of the old woman he had carried across, the stately form of Juno.

" Young man," said she, " you have a good and brave heart, and you shall not regret your kindness to an old woman " ; then she vanished.

When Jason recovered from his surprise and

started to go on, he saw, to his dismay, that one
of his sandals had been lost in the rushing water ;
so he had to walk the rest of the way with only
one shoe. He came at last to the palace of his
father's brother and was led before the king.

The king turned pale with fear at sight of
Jason ; for an oracle had foretold that his kingdom would be taken from him by a youth wearing
only one sandal, and one of Jason's feet, as you
know, was bare.

But the crafty king pretended to be very glad
indeed to see his nephew. He bade him sit down
and rest himself, and placed food and drink before
him. While they were eating, the king told many
stories of brave men who had lived long ago.
" Ah, those days are past," he sighed. " Such
heroes do not live in our times."

" You are wrong ! " cried Jason, " there are
many heroes waiting only for the chance to do
great deeds."

At this the king laughed aloud. " Is it possible,"
said he, " that you have never heard the story of
the Golden Fleece ? Long years have I been
waiting for a hero to bring it hither, for it would
add greatly to our wealth and happiness." And
then he told the story of Phryxus and Helle, and
of the Golden Fleece in the woods, guarded by the
sleepless dragon.

When he had finished, Jason sprang to his feet

and cried, " I will prove to you, O king, that the race of heroes is not dead. I will bring you the Golden Fleece, or die in the attempt."

The king was very much pleased ; for this was just what he wanted—to send Jason off on a journey so full of danger that there would be very little chance of his ever coming back. But, of course, he did not show how pleased he was.

Jason built a good, strong ship, which he called the *Argo*, because Argo means "the swift." At its prow was a figurehead cut from an oak-tree sacred to Juno. Juno had sent the gift to show Jason that she had not forgotten her promise to help him. It was a very wonderful piece of wood, as you will agree when I tell you that it could speak. Many a time during the long voyage, when Jason was in great danger and did not know what to do, he consulted that figurehead, and he always received good advice.

When the ship was finished, Jason sent word of his intended voyage to his comrades of the old school days, and they all came to join him. These heroes were called the Argonauts, from the ship *Argo* in which they sailed.

After a long and dangerous voyage, during which there happened many wonderful things about which you will some day hear, the Argonauts arrived at Colchis, the land of the Golden Fleece.

THE ARROW AND THE SONG

I SHOT an arrow into the air,
It fell to earth, I knew not where;
For so swiftly it flew, the sight
Could not follow it in its flight.

I breathed a song into the air,
It fell to earth, I knew not where;
For who has sight so keen and strong,
That it can follow the flight of song?

Long, long afterwards, in an oak
I found the arrow, still unbroke;
And the song, from beginning to end,
I found again in the heart of a friend.

HENRY WADSWORTH LONGFELLOW

The Story of the Golden Fleece

III. HOW THE FLEECE WAS BROUGHT BACK TO GREECE

THE morning after their arrival at Colchis, the Greeks were brought into the palace of the king. The king had two children, a little boy of whom he was very fond, and a dark-eyed, dark-haired maiden, Medea, who was a witch and knew many magic arts.

The king was seated on his throne, with his little son at his feet and Medea at his right hand, when the Argonauts were brought before him. Jason was asked what his errand in Colchis was ; and when he answered that he had come to take the Golden Fleece back to Greece, the king laughed aloud, and said, " You have come on a very bold mission, for only he who performs aright the three tasks I have set can carry away the Golden Fleece."

And the tone in which the king gave this answer showed that he was not afraid of losing the Golden Fleece. But Jason was not to be so easily discouraged, and he asked the king to tell him what the three tasks were.

" The first is to yoke two fierce, fire-breathing bulls to the plough, and with them to till four acres of land.   The next is to sow some dragons' teeth, and to conquer all the armed men that will then spring up from the earth.   And the third is to kill the fierce dragon which guards the Golden Fleece in the wood, and never sleeps by night or by day. When you have succeeded in doing these three things, you may take the Golden Fleece back with you to Greece."   Thus spoke the king and then dismissed Jason.

Although Jason would not let the king see it, he was just a little discouraged when he heard what the tasks were.   He walked away from the palace, down towards the shore where his boat was anchored, and he thought of Juno's promise and wished that she would help him now.

When he came to the ship, he found that there was help awaiting him.   For Medea, the king's daughter, had fallen in love with him, and had come to talk with him and to offer him her aid.

She promised to give Jason advice that would help to do the things that seemed impossible, if in return he would make her his wife and take her back with him to his home in Greece.

It may seem strange that Medea was willing to leave her home and all the people who loved her, to go so far away with this stranger.   Indeed, the girl herself hardly knew why she did it ; but the

truth was that Juno had not forgotten her promise
to help Jason, and the only way she could do it
was by making Medea love him so much that she
would be willing to give up everything for his
sake. And so it really was Juno who was helping
Jason.

The king's daughter gave Jason some magic
drugs to make him proof against harm from fire
or sword, and then told him just what he must do
to overcome the fierce bulls and the armed men.
After she left him, he paced up and down the seashore for a long time, thinking about Medea, and
the tasks that the morrow would bring.

The next morning all the people of Colchis went
in a great crowd to the field where Jason was to
meet his death, as they thought. In the midst of
them sat the king himself, with Medea at his
right hand. In all that vast crowd, she was the
only one who dared to hope that Jason would be
successful.

As soon as Jason entered the field, the two bulls
came snorting and bellowing towards him. If you
could have seen the creatures, you would have
believed, as all the people did, that Jason's last
hour had come.

They were great, ugly creatures, with hoofs of
brass, and horns pointed with iron. As they
came trampling along, making the ground tremble
at each step of their brazen hoofs, they breathed

out curling flames from their nostrils, so that the fields and the whole air seemed to be on fire.

But Jason did not feel the heat of the flames, thanks to Medea's magic drug. He went up close to the angry creatures, and seizing them by the horns, dashed their heads together until the bulls were stunned. Then he quickly slipped the yoke over their heads. The bulls were now as gentle as cows, and Jason ploughed the four acres in a short time.

Next he sowed the dragons' teeth in the soil he had just turned up, and in less time than it takes to tell, a mass of helmets began to show above the ground, just as the little leaves pierce through the soil in the springtime. But, whereas the leaves are followed by pretty blossoms, the helmets covered a very ugly crop of fierce, armed soldiers, who all turned upon Jason at once. Remembering Medea's advice, he seized a large stone and hurled it into the midst of his foes.

This made them turn from Jason against one another, for each one thought it was his neighbour who had thrown the stone. Soon they were all fighting and struggling in a confused mass, and they fought so fiercely that in a short time the field was strewn with the dead bodies of the men who had sprung up from the dragons' teeth.

Of course, the people were all rejoiced at Jason's success, but the king looked angry and sullen.

He knew very well that Jason could not have succeeded except by the aid of magic, and he suspected that in some way Medea had helped the hero. Therefore, when Jason asked for leave to begin his third task, the king answered that he had done enough for one day, and that he should rest until the morrow.

But in the evening, Medea, who could see that her father suspected her, told Jason he must kill the dragon that night and sail for home ; for she had noticed her father's angry look and she feared that he meant some harm to the Argonauts.

Again she gave him a drug to put the dragon to sleep, and Jason made his way alone into the dark wood. He had not gone far when he noticed a golden light among the forest trees, and he knew that he must be near the treasure he was seeking.

So he went along carefully, and when he came within a few feet of the dragon, he threw the magic drug into its eyes ; and after a few moments, the dragon was fast asleep. Jason thereupon cut off the creature's head and seized the Golden Fleece from the branches overhead, where it hung, making the forest bright as though the sun were shining upon it ; then he hastened back to his ship, where Medea and his companions were anxiously waiting.

In a very short time the anchor was lifted, and

with their sails flapping merrily in the breeze, the Greeks had started on their homeward way, carrying the Golden Fleece with them.

After a long, hard journey, full of adventures, they at last reached home. Jason banished his uncle from the kingdom, and set his father back on the throne. Thus he fulfilled his vow, and King Æson, grown young again through happiness at his son's return, ruled in peace for many a year.

How a Boy loved a Stag

ONCE Apollo dearly loved a lad whose name was Cyparissus, and the youth, in turn, was very fond of Apollo. He liked to hunt, and he loved the woods and the brooks and all the shy, wild creatures that lived in the forests. All these things he loved, but dearer to him than anything else was a stag that lived in the grove where he hunted.

The stag was a beautiful creature, with great, soft eyes and branching antlers. He belonged to the nymphs of the grove, and they had hung about his neck a golden necklace, studded with shining gems. He was the pet of all the people who lived near that place, and was so tame that he would go round from door to door and offer his glossy neck to be patted. He was afraid of no one, for everyone loved him and was kind to him.

Cyparissus and the stag were together from morning till night. They wandered through the woods, seeking the shady nooks and the little streams, where the stag could see his beautiful antlers reflected and could drink the cool water. The boy would weave garlands of flowers for the

stag's neck; or, springing lightly on his playfellow's back, he would speed through the woods
more swiftly than the wind.

Apollo often joined this happy pair in the forest,
and laughed and played with them, just as though
he, too, were a child.

One hot summer's day, Cyparissus and the stag
had been wandering through the grove for many
hours, and at noon they paused in a shady spot
by the side of a stream.   The stag was resting on
the soft grass, under a tree, and Cyparissus stood
a little way off, practising with his bow and arrow.

Just how it happened he never knew; but, suddenly, as he was fitting the arrow to the bow his foot
slipped, the sharp steel glided off sidewise, and
with a little hiss, it entered the poor stag's breast.

Cyparissus, filled with horror, rushed to his companion's side and drew the cruel steel from his
breast.   But it was too late—the arrow had done
its work only too well.   The wounded stag lifted
its head, and gave the boy a last, loving, questioning look, then fell back on the grass—dead.

Poor Cyparissus ! He had killed the creature he
loved most in all the world, and his grief was sad to
see. He threw himself on the ground beside the dead
stag, kissed the soft forehead over and over again,
and moaned aloud.   He felt that he could not live
without his dear playfellow, and was ready to pierce
himself with the same arrow that had slain the stag.

But Apollo, who heard his friend's voice weeping in the forest, came hastening to the spot. When he saw what had happened, he tried to console Cyparissus, telling that he must not blame himself for what had been a mere accident ; and at last he induced him to give up the arrow with which he meant to kill himself. But the poor boy wept and mourned, and would not be comforted, and at last he died of grief.

Apollo grieved much over his little friend's sad death ; he wept over the lifeless body, and loosed the boy's arm from round the stag's neck and cried, " Never again shall I hear your merry laughter ringing through the woods, nor see you wandering in the grove with your playmate. The birds will miss your happy song, and the leaves and the flowers will seem less bright now that you are gone from them. All the shy, wild creatures of the grove will steal from their hiding-places, and wonder that you no longer come to greet them. But I will mourn for you for ever, Cyparissus, and you shall mourn for others, and shall henceforth be the emblem of sorrow and death."

Then Apollo changed Cyparissus into a cypress tree, that he might continue to live in the green forests, with the birds and the flowers he loved so dearly. And to this day the cypress tree is planted above graves as an emblem of grief.

EARTH TO EARTH

HIS hands with earthly work are done,
　His feet are done with roving—
We bring him now to thee, and ask
　The loved to take the loving.

Part back thy mantle, fringed with green,
　Broidered with leaf and blossom,
And lay him tenderly to sleep,
　Dear Earth, upon thy bosom.

Thy cheerful birds, thy liberal flowers,
　Thy woods and waters, only,
Gave him their sweet companionship,
　And made his hours less lonely.

Then part thy mantle, fringed with green,
　Broidered with leaf and blossom,
And lay him tenderly to sleep,
　Dear Earth, upon thy bosom.

PHŒBE CARY

EVEN such is time, that takes on trust
　Our youth, our joys, our all we have,
And pays us but with age and dust ;
Who in the dark and silent grave,
When we have wandered all our ways,
Shuts up the story of our days :
But from this earth, this grave, this dust,
The Lord shall raise me up, I trust !

SIR WALTER RALEIGH

A Sea God and a Wicked Enchantress

THERE was once a poor fisherman named Glaucus, who earned his daily bread by selling the fish he caught. One day his net felt very heavy, and when he drew it in, he saw that he had caught a great number of fine fish. He emptied them out upon the grass by his side, and then prepared his net for another throw.

But the fish he had caught began flapping about and nibbling at the grass beneath them, and in a few minutes, what was the fisherman's surprise to see them all leap back into the water and swim away!

" Why, what wonderful grass that must be ! " cried Glaucus, and he took up a handful and began to chew it. As soon as the juice entered his blood, a strange feeling of restlessness came over him ; and at length he had such a mad longing to throw himself into the clear water, that almost before he knew what he was doing, he plunged into the sea with a great splash.

Neptune, the god of the ocean, saw all that was passing ; and as Glaucus sank beneath the surface, he caught him in his arms, and, taking him into his ocean palace, changed him from a poor fisherman into a god of the sea.

Glaucus now lived entirely in the water—that very water he had loved so dearly when he was a fisherman. His beard grew long, and of the colour of the seaweed that the tide washes ashore ; his hair, which streamed behind him, looked almost like the waves on which it floated. He was made the god of the fishermen ; and, remembering his own struggles in former days, he sent many a poor fisherman home with a full net and a happy heart.

So years passed, until one day, as the sea god was floating on the top of the waves, he saw a beautiful maiden walking along the shore.

She looked so modest and gentle that Glaucus' heart was deeply moved, and he followed her until she came to a low hill. She climbed to the top and then turned to give a parting look at the sea, which she loved very much ; but she did not notice the dark face watching her so closely, and, turning down the hill, she disappeared from view.

Glaucus sighed and slowly swam back to his home under the sea.

The next day he came again to the spot, and as before, the nymph, whose name was Scylla, was walking by the side of the sea. Again he followed her, watching her until she disappeared behind the little hill.

So it went on, day after day, and the more
Glaucus saw of Scylla, the more he loved her. At
last, one evening, as Scylla was about to climb the
hill, Glaucus called to her. She turned round
and was very much surprised to see that strange
figure, half man and half fish.

She stepped nearer to the water and said,
" Pray, what are you, a man or a sea monster ? "
Then Glaucus related his whole story, and ended
by telling her how much he loved her. But Scylla
did not care for this strange looking creature,
whom she saw that day for the first time ; and she
turned away from him, and left him sad and hopeless.

For many days he came in vain to the spot
where he had so often seen Scylla, but the maiden
no longer walked there. Then Glaucus tried another way of winning her.

Near his home there lived an enchantress whose
name was Circe. He hastened to her palace, told
her his story, and begged for a love potion—a
drink which should make Scylla love him. Now
it so happened that Circe herself had for a long
time been in love with Glaucus ; so she told him
that Scylla was not worthy of his love, and that
if he would stay in her palace, she would make
him happy all the rest of his life. But Glaucus
answered, " Sooner shall seaweed grow on the
mountain tops and trees in the ocean, than my love

for Scylla change while she is alive." Then at last
Circe saw that she must at least pretend to grant
his wish.

In her heart she hated Scylla, and she had made
up her mind to do something very cruel. She
handed Glaucus a little flask filled with a colour-
less liquid, and told him to throw it into the
water where Scylla bathed.

Glaucus hastened home, and finding the spring
where Scylla usually took her evening bath, he
emptied the little flask, which he thought so
precious, and then went away with a happy heart.
Poor Glaucus ! He little knew what a mischief-
making witch Circe was.

Towards evening Scylla came to the little spring,
and throwing off her robe, slipped into the clear
water to enjoy its cool freshness.

But the mixture Circe had given Glaucus was
most horrible, for it bred monsters. Scarcely had
Scylla stepped into the water than her legs began
to change their shape ; and at last she screamed
aloud in terror, for where her limbs had been, there
were now six horrible, loud-mouthed, fierce-looking
dogs.

At first she thought they were only in the water,
and she rushed to the shore. When she saw that
the monsters were part of her own body, she
ran screaming to the top of the hill, and threw
herself headlong into the foaming waves of the sea.

She was changed to a rock, but ever after, that part of the sea was dangerous to sail through, and many people who have narrowly escaped shipwreck there have told how they heard the loud fierce barking of dogs from the base of the rock.

Poor Glaucus mourned for Scylla many a day, and never again went near the cruel Circe. To this day, the rock Scylla stands in the blue Mediterranean, and is shunned by all who sail upon the sea.

THE SEA HATH ITS PEARLS

THE sea hath its pearls,
  The heaven hath its stars;
But my heart, my heart,
  My heart hath its love.

Great are the sea and the heaven,
  Yet greater is my heart;
And fairer than pearls and stars
  Flashes and beams my love.

Thou little, youthful maiden,
  Come unto my great heart;
My heart, and the sea, and the heaven
  Are melting away with love!

HENRY WADSWORTH LONGFELLOW

A Youth who was changed into a Flower

YOU remember the sad story about Apollo's
friend Cyparissus, and how the sun-god
grieved when the poor boy died. This
story is about another boy whom Apollo lóved very
dearly.

Hyacinthus was his name, and I think you will
agree with me that it is a very pretty name. You
know a flower with a name very much like that ?
Perhaps they have something to do with each
other. Let us read the story and see.

Hyacinthus was a happy, sunny-hearted lad,
who seemed to have no care in the wide world.
Perhaps that is why Apollo loved him so much ;
or perhaps he reminded him of that other boy who
had died long before ; or perhaps it was just
because Apollo had to love somebody, and he
might just as well choose this merry little hunter
whom he met so often in the woods.

But whatever the reason was, it is certain that
Apollo did love Hyacinthus very, very dearly.
He would leave his beautiful temples, and forget
all about the people who were worshipping him,
and be content to wander in the woods by the

side of his little friend ; and he was happy to carry his hunting-nets, or hold his dogs for a while.

Hyacinthus did not think it at all strange that Apollo should like to do these things for him. For love is so wonderful a thing, that it makes people forget all differences of birth or rank.

So Apollo and Hyacinthus hunted together very happily and neither of them ever thought of the wide difference between a little hunter boy and a great god of heaven.

One day, while they were resting in a shady nook, Apollo proposed to play a game of quoits. Quoits was a game of which the people of those days were very fond—as fond as boys are nowadays of cricket and of ball. The quoits were flat circular discs about twelve inches across ; they were made of iron or some other heavy substance. The players hurled their discs into the air, the object of the game being to see who could throw the quoits the farthest.

Apollo and his companion were both fond of the game, and they began to play, and were enjoying themselves very much. Apollo hurled his disc high into the air, and it shot up through the clouds, and, after a long pause, fell to the ground with a crash.

Then Hyacinthus, eager to show that he was as good a player as his friend, hurried forward to pick it up. But the disc had struck the ground with such force that it rebounded, and hit the thought-less boy on the forehead.

Stunned by the blow, Hyacinthus with a little cry of pain, sank to the ground. Apollo rushed to his side, and kneeling down, tried to stanch the wound with his hand, while he tenderly car-essed the lad. He was so frightened that he was almost as pale as the wounded Hyacinthus

When he saw that he could not stop the wound from bleeding, he quickly gathered some herbs and pressed their juice between the dying boy's lips. But it was of no use—Hyacinthus was fast sinking, his head drooping like a bruised flower, and like a flower he faded away.

Apollo's grief was sad to see. He could not believe, at first, that the boy he loved so dearly was really dead, and he called him by name again and again. He would gladly have died for him, and he did not care to live without him ; but you know the gods could never die. He lay on the ground by the side of his dead friend, and wept and moaned, so that it would have made you cry, too, if you had seen him.

Then, at last, he seized his lyre, for now that Hyacinthus was gone, he turned to this old friend for comfort. And he sang a song of love and mourning for the boy, so sadly beautiful that all the birds in the forest were hushed, and even the wind in the tree tops seemed to sigh in sympathy.

When he had finished, he stooped down and tenderly touched the boy's forehead with his hand ; in an instant the lifeless body vanished, and in its stead had sprung up a lovely, purple blossom. It was almost the colour of the blood that had flowed from the boy's forehead.

And since that day, so long ago, the beautiful purple hyacinth comes with the first breath of spring, to remind us of the story of the great god of the sun and the little lad whom he loved so dearly.

TO A FRIEND

GREEN be the turf above thee,
    Friend of my better days !
None knew thee but to love thee,
    Nor named thee but to praise.

Tears fell, when thou wert dying,
    From eyes unused to weep,
And long, where thou art lying,
    Will tears the cold turf steep.

When hearts, whose truth was proven,
    Like thine, are lain in earth,
There should a wreath be woven
    To tell the world their worth.

FITZ-GREENE HALLECK

The Story of Pygmalion and Galatea

I. THE STATUE

IN the busy seaport of Amathus, that stood
upon the southern shore of Cyprus, there once
lived a sculptor, Pygmalion, whose work was
all in all to him. Other joys he scarcely knew ;
he took little pleasure in the praise men lavished
on his beautiful handiwork, and he did not choose
to make friends. Many fair maidens would have
been glad to marry this maker of beautiful statues,
but he cared for none of them. There came a
day, however, when for the first time he felt lonely
and dispirited. He had been watching the busy
life of the streets and quays, and in contrast his
own days seemed dull and void of interest. His
quiet house oppressed him with a growing sense
of loneliness ; what use to him were those lovely
statues of Juno, Pallas, or Diana ? What companionship could he find in a marble Hermes ?

These gloomy thoughts did not long occupy the
sculptor. Like a shaft of light from the rising sun,
an inspiration came suddenly to him, and selecting
a block of snow-white marble that had just been

brought to his workshop, he began with feverish
haste to give form to the shapeless mass. And as
his practised hand wielded mallet and chisel he
exclaimed : " Thine aid, Goddess of Love ! Do
thou direct my hand, and from this stone shall
come forth a maiden figure worthy of thine
acceptance."

Little could Pygmalion think how fully his
prayer would be answered. The goddess heard the
supplication, and forthwith she filled his mind
with a vision of womanly beauty beyond anything
he had imagined, and lent to his chisel skill to
reproduce it in the lifeless marble. As the form
took shape beneath his hand its surpassing loveliness stirred him to the depths of his being, and he
gave himself up wholly to the inspiration of Venus.

Each morning he rose early, and, absorbed in
his work, he laboured ceaselessly so long as daylight lasted. Night seemed but a cruel interruption
to his toil, and the dark hours were endurable only
when brightened by dreams of the maidenly form
that haunted his waking thoughts. Once, when
the statue was all but completed, he grew ashamed
of the eagerness he was displaying ; he would
leave his workshop for a whole day, he resolved,
and go to the woods with his bow and arrows, in
hopes that the change of scene and occupation
might bring him to a more wholesome frame of
mind. Vain hope ! Never did he spend a more

wearisome day than that on which he banished
himself from his beloved toil ; the west wind swept
softly over scented flowers, the bees busied themselves in the clover, and the mower's scythe
flashed through the ripened grass, but Pygmalion
sat moodily, as though the whole world had been
changed to stone. Things living had no interest
for him now ; his heart was given to the lifeless
form in marble.

Long ere sunset he was hastening homeward,
murmuring to himself : " What a fool was I to
leave her ! What if she were gone when I returned ? " Then he bit his lips with vexation
that he should have fallen into the trick of speaking
as if the statue were a woman of flesh and blood.
No sooner had he reached his house than, catching
up his chisel, he set to work, with such energy that
before daylight had faded he had put the last
masterly touches to his statue, and was feasting
his eyes upon the completed marvel.

The image stood with one hand outstretched
towards him, and in the other was a great loose-
petalled rose. Her lips were parted, but without
a smile, and her calm, grave face looked down
upon the sculptor with eyes that seemed to harbour
something of human love itself.

" Ah ! " cried Pygmalion, " why have I fashioned
thee ? Thou hast taught me what love means ;
but other men learn that lesson from the fair

women whom the gods send to them endowed
with life, whereas I, poor wretch, can worship
only the figure that my own hands have carved
in stone ! Oh, if I could but perfect my work
and give life unto thy form ! "

And as his lips framed the hopeless words, the
impossibility of his longing went home to his
weary soul. For a time grief overwhelmed him,
but from its very violence the outburst could not
last long, and as he grew calmer the thought that
he alone might enjoy the sight of this wondrous
treasure brought him some comfort. With a pang
of jealousy that any other than himself should
touch his treasure he called a number of stout
men from the street, and watched them bear it
to his chamber, where it was safely enshrined in
a small niche. He then ransacked his chests in
search of the costliest ornaments he owned, and,
deeming his best all too poor for the marble maid,
he visited every jeweller's booth in Amathus until
he had collected gems worthy, as he felt, to adorn
his beloved. On the rounded arms and the slender
fingers he placed bracelets and costly rings ; and
he encircled the delicate throat with the rarest
of jewelled necklaces. In the morning, not content with these costly expressions of his devotion,
he hurried to his garden, and brought bunches of
sweet flowers to lay at her feet.

" Dear image of the womanhood I worship,"

he cried, " although thou canst never move nor
speak, yet I will love thee to the day of my death,
and thou shalt be to me like the living woman that
thou well mightest be." Then placing beneath
her pedestal a dainty little altar, inlaid with gold,
which he had made by order of some wealthy
patron, he burnt upon it sweet cedarwood, and
scattered Arabian frankincense on the flame, to do
his love the honours of a goddess, for, said he,
she was fairer than a mortal, and it was meet
that she should have reverence shown her. Morning and evening he worshipped her divine beauty,
but during the day he looked upon her as a woman,
and would sometimes praise her loveliness, sometimes turn and reproach her playfully for her
silence, and again he would tell her he was but
a dull companion, and would take up a book of
lovers' tales, and read aloud to her many a chapter.

The love that he had been unable to lavish upon
any woman thus found a strange outlet in his
devotion to the marble maiden. How foolish it
was, and yet how natural, that he should find
such pleasure even in pretending that his lonely
house was at last ·brightened by the presence of
a gracious lady.

The Story of Pygmalion and Galatea

II. THE WOMAN

THE second morning after Pygmalion had brought the image to his chamber he was awakened by songs outside his window. Springing up he saw that the priests of Amathus were leading through the streets a car on which was placed a statue of Venus—one that his own hands had carved, he noted, though to-day his handiwork was hidden by a long, flame-coloured silken robe that fell from the goddess's shoulders to the ground.

It was the custom of the town that three times in the year the people should be awakened by this procession, in which young men and maids danced and sang round the car of Venus, the patron goddess of their island. As Pygmalion watched the throng stream past, there came to his mind stories of the kind deeds done by the Goddess of Love for wretched, lovelorn men, and of how she had often helped her worshippers to gain their desire. Why should not he ask her aid this morning? Quickly he made ready to join the crowd that was gathering behind the car ; he had never before taken part in these ceremonies, and it was with an odd sensation of light-heartedness that he dressed himself in gay clothes and bound a wreath of flowers across his brow. Then, stooping to kiss the cold white feet of his marble love, he left his house and hastened after the procession, which was slowly wending its way round the town.

To the impatient Pygmalion it seemed that the car was drawn through every street and by-road in Amathus, and, indeed, he had time before the temple gates were reached to grow somewhat ashamed of being seen among the young and frivolous followers of Venus. In due course the statue had been lifted back to its niche above the altar, and the hymns of praise were being sung, but even now he fretted till all should be over and he should find himself alone to make his solemn prayer to the goddess.

At length the tedious rites were ended, and the temple was deserted by all but a few priestesses and one or two strangers busied with their own petitions. He crossed the inlaid floor, now thickly strewn with fresh flowers, and, standing before the altar, he cast an offering of sweet incense upon the flame.

" Venus, Goddess of Love, to whom all things are possible, refuse not my prayer ! Since daybreak have I followed in thy train and listened to the hymns sung in praise of thy kindness to the lovelorn. Show me that kindness, I pray thee, O goddess! Take pity on one who so madly loves a lifeless form, and grant me my heart's desire. Ah! Venus, canst not thou bestow the gift of life on my beloved ? "

Hardly were his faltering words ended when the flame that he was feeding with incense shot high upon the altar, so high that it seemed almost to reach the dome of the temple. Ere it sank it had filled Pygmalion's breast with hope, for no better omen could he have wished than this lively flame leaping, as it were, in answer to his prayer ; and when, presently, he saw a thick black cloud roll round the altar and the statue of the goddess overhead, he wondered if perchance Venus were veiling herself that she might come down from her high station and work the gracious deed to reward her supplant. But even while he waited expectantly the cloud vanished, and the temple became to his eyes as before, a dim, gold-decked sanctuary, where men, but never a goddess, might be seen moving. His hopes fell as fast as they had arisen, and with a sigh of despair he turned from the temple and passed out through its sheltering groves of myrtle. He saw the townsfolk in the streets laughing and making merry with one another, while he alone was walking back to an empty, silent home, without a living soul to welcome him.

" Life without companionship, how miserable ! " he murmured, thinking of his lot ; and though he was eager to look again upon the face he loved, it saddened him to remember that that face could not be moved by his devotion.

Suddenly, as he reached his own threshold, a strange change of feeling came over him. He saw with a clear mind what madness it was that he should lose his heart to an image ; his love-sickness seemed at an end, and he exclaimed, " Thanks to thee, Venus, that thou hast given me an answer to my prayer for aid, unlike though it be to the boon which I was craving ! To pray thee to give life unto a statue was folly. Thou hast indeed denied my request, but in thy kindness thou hast opened my eyes to the vanity of my desire ; wilt thou not, then, some day send me a helpmate of flesh and blood now that I have learnt the sweetness of love for another ? "

But if Pygmalion fancied that he had come to think less of his marble maiden, he quickly discovered how very dear he still held her. From the outer door he passed to his own chamber, and with habit too deeply impressed to be all in a moment discarded, he raised his eyes to the niche where—where no image was to be seen !

" Gone ! " he cried dully, his heart aching as it

had never ached before. " All that was mine to love, gone."

" Pygmalion ! "

Whose is that low, soft voice breaking the accustomed silence ?

The poor artist turned quickly to the sound, and on the floor against the western windows he saw his beloved standing in the golden light of sunset, an image no longer, but changed to a living woman, whose breath came gently from the lips that he himself had chiselled. Her slim feet, pressed so often by his kisses, were moving towards him ; a rosy flush tinged her cheeks, the masses of her soft hair were stirred by the breeze from the open casement, and her eyes shone bright with the new-born life within. Even at that supreme moment Pygmalion noticed that her dress was none other than the saffron robe which had decked the statue of Venus in the morning.

Timidly the maiden drew near, and these were the words that fell in silver tones upon his enraptured ears :

" Pygmalion, Venus has heard thy prayer. She has given me life to-day that I may become thy loving and beloved bride."

At first the sculptor could not believe that what he saw and heard was not a dream, but all doubt vanished when his new-made wife laid her warm cheek against his and whispered, " Nay, this is no dream, dearest. Wilt thou not speak to me as lovingly as thou didst when I stood lifeless in yonder niche? " Then, in overwhelming rapture, he kissed her, and gave her a glad welcome to his home.

" Tell me," he questioned after a time, " tell me the story of thine awakening."

" Dearest," she answered, " I have but little store of wisdom, and the words that I have learned are few as yet ; but listen, I will tell thee as best I may.

" When first my eyes beheld what was round me I stood in the niche beyond thy couch, and from my hand, I remember, something was falling —heavy it was and, I think, shaped like one of those sweet flowers. Before me stood a most lovely lady. ' Come down,' she cried smilingly— ' come down, and learn in this house, Galatea, the happy lessons of life and love.'

" At her bidding I stepped down, and she, teaching me the words which I repeated at thy coming, robed me in her own silken raiment, as a sign to thee that it was indeed the Goddess Venus who had awakened me to life. Then pressing her lips to mine, she said, ' Life without love were a gift of little worth. With this kiss receive from me the power of loving even as thou art loved and my sure promise that thy life and Pygmalion's shall ever be blessed above the common lot of mortals.' And, so saying, she disappeared from my sight.

" Ah ! Pygmalion, surely the Goddess of Cyprus is gracious to her people."

BEAUTY

SHE walks in beauty, like the night
Of cloudless climes and starry skies ;
And all that's best of dark and bright
Meet in her aspect and her eyes ;
Thus mellow'd to that tender light
Which heaven to gaudy day denies.

One shade the more, one ray the less,
Had half impair'd the nameless grace
Which waves in every raven tress,
Or softly lightens o'er her face,
Where thoughts serenely sweet express
How pure, how dear their dwelling-place.

And on that cheek, and o'er that brow
So soft, so calm, yet eloquent,
The smiles that win, the tints that glow
But tell of days in goodness spent—
A mind at peace with all below,
A heart whose love is innocent !

LORD BYRON

A Musical Contest of Long Ago

MOST of my young readers know the wonderful story of King Midas and the Golden Touch, how everything he laid his hands on was turned to shining, yellow metal. But there is another story about him, which, though not so well known as that of the Golden Touch, also shows that King Midas was sometimes not so wise a monarch as he should have been.

You remember reading in another story how Pan, the god of the woods, first made the flute from the reeds that grew by the river. Now this same Pan was a great favourite with King Midas, and the king thought him the finest musician in the world. The nymphs of the woods, also, loved to hear Pan play on his flute, and at last he became so used to hearing his praises sung that he, too, thought himself the greatest musician in the world ; and one day he went so far as to ask the great god Apollo to enter with him into a contest of musical skill.

Apollo, the sun-god, was, as you know, the sweetest singer in the world ; therefore it was a

very bold thing indeed for Pan to challenge him.
Yet Apollo agreed to take part in the trial.

The place of meeting was a lofty hill, not far
from the palace of King Midas. As judge, they
chose the ruler of the mountain, a mighty king with
long, white locks and flowing beard, and large
dreamy eyes that seemed to have looked on the
hills about him for hundreds of summers and
winters.

Midas, clothed in a purple robe, sat at the judge's
right hand, while grouped about them were the
nymphs and the satyrs, and all who were eager
to be present at the coming contest. In front of
the judge stood Apollo, with his golden cloak and
shining lyre, and Pan himself, with his goatskin
flung loosely about his shoulders. A strange and
beautiful picture it must have been, and I wish all
of you could have been there to see it.

Pan was the first to play, and, amid a breathless
silence, he lifted his pipe of reeds to his lips.

There was something in his music that belonged
to the woods and the rivers; you could almost
hear the gurgling of the brooks and the sighing of
the wind in the trees, with now and then a strange
cry, as though a wild beast had been suddenly
startled from its lair. Yet for the first time, the
listeners found his music a little rude and wild ;
somehow it did not seem to fit the place or the
occasion. Midas, alone, expressed great delight

at his favourite's playing, and called him to sit
by his side.

When Pan had finished, Apollo stepped to the
front. His hair gleamed like the sun's bright
rays, and his eyes shone like stars. He threw
open his rich golden mantle, and, seizing his lyre,
began to play such sweet, heavenly music that all
the listeners wept for joy. Even Pan threw down
his flute before this wonderful singer, who could
move people to laughter or to tears by touching
the strings of his lyre.

When Apollo had finished, all the people ran up
to him with cries of praise and thanks, and crowned
him with his own laurel wreath of victory. But
Midas, foolish King Midas, said that to his taste
Pan's music was far more beautiful than the sun
god's. To punish him for this stupid use of his
ears, Apollo changed them to long, furry asses'
ears.

In great excitement the king locked himself in
his royal chamber and then sent for the court
barber. After making him swear to keep his
secret, Midas showed his asses' ears, and told the
barber to make him a wig of such shape that it
would hide the ugly things.

In a short time the wig was on his majesty's
head and he sent away the barber with the threat
that he would kill him if he told anyone the secret.
The barber, full of fear, hastened from the palace.

But his secret preyed on his mind until he could neither eat nor sleep for thinking of it ; and yet he dared not confide it to anyone.

At last he could stand it no longer. One midnight, when every one was fast asleep, he took a spade, and walked to an open meadow which was far away from any dwelling place. In the centre of it he dug a deep hole, and then, putting his mouth close to the ground, he whispered,

" *King Midas wears great asses' ears.*"

The barber felt very much better after this, and, filling up the hole, went home with a lighter heart.

Time passed, and over the hole which the barber had dug there grew a thicket of hollow reeds ; and when the wind played through them they gave forth these strange words,

" *King Midas wears great asses' ears.*"

Soon all the king's subjects came to hear of this secret that the reeds whispered, and then they knew how Apollo had punished their king for his stupid judgment. But Midas could not have blamed the barber, even if he had known about his midnight errand ; for in truth the poor fellow had never breathed the secret to a single person.

THE SWEET SINGER

HE the best of all musicians,
He the sweetest of all singers,
Beautiful and childlike was he,
Brave as man is, soft as woman,
Pliant as a wand of willow,
Stately as a deer with antlers.

When he sang the village listened;
All the women came to hear him;
Now he stirred their souls to passion,
Now he melted them to pity.

From the hollow reeds he fashioned
Flutes so musical and mellow,
That the brook
Ceased to murmur in the woodland,
That the wood birds ceased from singing,
And the squirrel
Ceased his chatter in the oak tree,
And the rabbit
Sat upright to look and listen.

All the many sounds of nature
Borrowed sweetness from his singing;
All the hearts of men were softened
By the pathos of his music;
For he sang of peace and freedom,
Sang of beauty, love, and longing;
Sang of death and life undying
In the land of the Hereafter.

H. W. LONGFELLOW
(*Hiawatha*)

The Boastful Shepherd

YOU are now to hear of another musical contest, but this time the great Apollo is challenged by a mere mortal. The story runs that one day Minerva was diverting herself with a flute, whose sweet and thrilling melody penetrated the cool recesses of the adjoining forest, silencing the singing of the birds, and falling with delightful softness upon the ears of a young shepherd wholly concealed in the cool summer grass, upon the banks of the same stream which, higher up, laved the beautiful feet of the goddess as she sat idly playing.

Presently Minerva was vexed with the puffed cheeks which stared back at her from the glassy stream, and flinging the flute into the water she exclaimed, "Hence, ye destroyer of beauty! Shall I disgrace my charms by making such an odious face?"

The sudden silence struck like a blow upon the entranced ear of the youthful Marsyas, and looking round him he perceived the rejected flute floating down the stream within reach of his arm. He immediately rescued it from the water, and putting it to his lips the godlike strains poured out anew, and thereafter the shepherd thought of nothing but his charmed instrument. Day and night his strains echoed through brake and covert, and in the grassy fields his flocks knew well the liquid sound. So, too, did the sneaking wolf, and many times he raided the lambs while the neglectful shepherd sat immersed in his magical tunes. The mountain nymphs would listen for long hours, and all men and maidens who came within hearing were also ravished by the skill of the musician.

At length the praise lavished upon Marsyas turned his head, and he forgot to give due credit to his wonderful instrument. In fact, he became so conceited that he actually imagined that Apollo could not play so well, and in a more than usually foolish moment he gave public utterance to this silly thought. "Let Apollo come," he boasted, "and you will soon admit that I am the better player."

The words reached the ear of the god in one of the many moments when he had nothing particular to do, and he resolved to punish the shepherd for his presumption. In common with the other gods, he was always very jealous of the special powers attributed to him, and would not suffer a mortal to lay claim to them. He determined, therefore, to show forth the great superiority of his powers, that men might see how foolish Marsyas had been in making the comparison ; and thus in punishing the vain shepherd he would exalt himself.

First Apollo called upon the nine Muses, the patronesses of music, to act as judges, and together with them he appeared before Marsyas upon an occasion when he was surrounded by a band of admirers in a beautiful sylvan retreat, and called upon the musician to make good his boastful words. Nothing loth, the foolish youth quickly commenced to play upon his flute, and the strains which issued forth were sweet as those :

By summer hid in green reeds' jointed cells
To wait imprisoned for the south wind's spells.
From out his reedy flute the player drew,
And as the music clearer, louder grew,
Wild creatures from their winter nooks and dells,
Sweet furry things with eyes like starry wells,
Crept wanderingly out ; they thought the south wind blew.
With instant joyous trust, they flocked around
His feet who such a sudden summer made,
His eyes more kind than men's, enthralled and bound
Them there.[1]

The Muses were more than pleased with Marsyas, and they praised his tuneful skill, which, said they, Orpheus himself might have envied. They then called upon Apollo, and the divine minstrel, taking his lyre, answered their expectation with a stream of melody which would have charmed the heavenly

[1] Helen Hunt Jackson.

gods. The Muses, however, hesitated to decide between the musicians, and, consulting together, they decided that each should give a second exhibition of his skill. Again the shepherd raised his more than mortal strains, and again, in his turn, Apollo took up his golden instrument. This time, however, the god accompanied the melody with the accents of his immortal voice, and as the sublime harmony rose and fell, all knew that the award was won, and the god would be acclaimed.

And so, as the gleams of the setting sun faded upon the western hills, the strife was ended, and the Muses pronounced that Marsyas had been vanquished. Punishment followed swiftly upon the judgment. Without more ado, Apollo bound his rival to a tree and put him to a cruel death. His friends, the mountain nymphs, mourned their favourite's sad end, and, weeping, they shed such abundance of tears that a river was formed, which is called Marsyas in memory of the ill-fated musician.

THE MUSIC OF NATURE

THE harp at Nature's advent strung
  Has never ceased to play;
The song the stars of morning sung
  Has never died away.

And prayer is made, and praise is given,
  By all things near and far;
The ocean looketh up to heaven,
  And mirrors every star.

The green earth sends her incense up
  From many a mountain shrine;
From folded leaf and dewy cup
  She pours her sacred wine.

The mists above the morning rills
  Rise white as wings of prayer;
The altar curtains of the hills
  Are sunset's purple air.

The blue sky is the temple's arch,
  Its transept earth and air,
The music of its starry march
  The chorus of a prayer.

                JOHN GREENLEAF WHITTIER

A Giant who loved a Sea Nymph

ONCE upon a time there lived on earth a strange race of giants called Cyclops. They were a very queer people indeed, and were much larger and stronger than any of the giants you have read about in your fairy tales. They lived in mountain caves, guarding flocks of sheep and herds of cattle.

It was said that when they spoke in angry tones, the whole mountain shook and quivered with the roaring, and the land round about trembled as with an earthquake.

The Cyclops were almost covered with hair, like animals, and this, together with their one fiery eye, gave them a very fierce look. For these strange beings, instead of having two eyes, as you and I have, had but a single large one ; and that one gleamed from the middle of their foreheads with such an angry glare that it frightened you much more than a hundred ordinary eyes could have done.

Indeed, it was said that when the Cyclops were raging about in their mountain caves, fire shot forth from those eyes, and then they looked exactly like volcanoes sending forth flames from the great holes in their summits.

You would think that these fierce, wild-looking creatures, who guarded their flocks all day long when they were not roaring or shooting out flames, would not be very likely to have feelings of love or tenderness. Yet I am going to tell you a story which will prove that the Cyclops could love after all, although there was something rough and shaggy about the love, as well as about the lovers.

In the cave of a mountain which overhung the blue sea, there lived one of these Cyclops whose name was Polyphemus. Every day he sat upon the rocks, watching his flocks graze, and making a great deal of noise on his hundred-reeded pipe.

And as he sat there, he watched the sea nymphs sporting in the water. They would rise on the crests of the waves, looking almost like white foam on the sea. Sometimes they combed out their yellow hair, which glistened like gold or like the sunlight on the clear, sparkling water.

The fairest and whitest of all the sea nymphs was Galatea. To the rough old Polyphemus she seemed just like a bit of sunshine and clear sky, and he fell very deeply in love with her.

He forgot to look after his sheep, but let them wander at their own sweet will. His huge staff— a pine-tree stripped of its boughs—lay idle at his side. He was anxious to look pleasing to the fair

Galatea ; so he combed out his tangled locks with a rake, cut his shaggy beard with a scythe, and then gazed into the clear, still water to see how he looked. It seemed to him that he looked very well indeed, for, of course, hugeness and shagginess and one flaming eye formed the very highest type of beauty for a Cyclops.

Then Polyphemus took his pipe of reeds, and sat down on a rock that overhung the water, and sang a song to his love. At the sound of his voice the mountains shook and the waves trembled, and the frightened sea nymphs hid themselves in their green caves. And this is the song he sang :

" O Galatea, you are fairer than the petals of the whitest blossom, more beautiful than the green fields or the young trees, and more pleasing to me than the winter's sun or the summer's shade. Why, then, do you fly from me ?

" If you knew me, you would listen to my pleading. My cave is in the heart of the mountain, where the heat of the midday sun is never felt, nor the icy cold of mid-winter ; there you will find trees laden with rosy apples, and vines with clusters of golden and purple grapes ; there you may gather the wild red strawberries in the woodland shade ; there will I bring you chestnuts and the fruit of all the other trees.

" See how great is my wealth—all these cows belong to me, and all these sheep. You shall have sweet milk to drink and fresh white cheese to eat. For playmates you shall have the young deer and the hares and the lambkins and a pair of snow-white doves, as well as the twin cubs of a bear which I have found on the mountain summit.

" O Galatea, lift your fair face from the blue sea. Come, do not scorn the gifts I offer. See, too, how huge I am. Great Jupiter in heaven is not larger. See the long hair which hangs over my shoulders, and, like a grove of trees, throws a shadow about my head. Surely, you must think this beautiful. A tree is bare without leaves, and a horse is ugly without a flowing mane ; feathers adorn the birds, and the sheep are clothed with wool ; so, too, a beard and shaggy hair are becoming to a Cyclops. I have but one eye in the middle of my forehead, yet the great sun in heaven, which sees all things, likewise has but one eye.

" My father rules over the blue sea in which you sport. Listen to my prayer, for I will make you happy. Come from your ocean home, O whitest nymph, come unto me who long for you."

Thus sang Polyphemus. But Galatea was only frightened at the great shaggy monster, for such he seemed to her, and at the roar of his awful voice. Besides, she was in love with a young shepherd named Acis ; and so, when Polyphemus had finished his song, she ran away to join her lover by the banks of a stream that flowed into the sea.

But Polyphemus, when he found that the lovely Galatea fled from him in spite of all he offered her, became very angry indeed. His voice began to roar, and his eye became fierce and flaming.

He wandered into the woods, and all the wild animals hurried into places of shelter when they felt the ground tremble under his angry step, and the little birds stopped singing, in their fright.

At last he came to the spot where the shepherd and Galatea were sitting lovingly together. Then his heart burned with wrath, and he seized a large rock and hurled it at the lovers. Galatea slipped beneath the waters and so escaped, but the shepherd was crushed under the heavy weight.

Yet Acis did not die, for the gods changed him into a stream of water, which gushed forth from under the rock. At first it was red and looked like blood, but as it flowed on, it became clearer and clearer, until at last, pure as crystal, it sprang into the sea and joined Galatea in her cave under the waters ; and there the gentle youth and the white sea nymph lived as happily as though poor, ugly, old Polyphemus had never seen them.

THE SHEPHERD'S SONG TO HIS LOVE

COME, live with me and be my love,
And we will all the pleasures prove
That hills and valleys, dale and field,
And all the craggy mountains yield.

There will I make thee beds of roses
And a thousand fragrant posies,
A cap of flowers, and a kirtle
Embroidered all with leaves of myrtle ;

A gown made of the finest wool,
Which from our pretty lambs we pull ;
Fair linèd slippers for the cold,
With buckles of the purest gold ;

A belt of straw and ivy buds ·
With coral clasps and amber studs ;
And if these pleasures may thee move,
Come, live with me and be my love.

Thy silver dishes for thy meat,
As precious as the gods do eat,
Shall on an ivory table be
Prepared each day for thee and me.

The shepherd swains shall dance and sing
For they delight each May morning :
If these delights thy mind may move,
Then, live with me and be my love.

CHRISTOPHER MARLOWE

A Jealous Goddess

ONCE upon a time there was a hunter named Cephalus, who was renowned not only for his skill in the chase, but also for the beauty of his person. So handsome was he that he attracted the love of Aurora, goddess of the dawn, but his heart having been given to Procris, a nymph in Diana's train, he could not return the goddess's affection. In due time Procris and Cephalus were wedded, and the nymph brought to her husband a hunting dog of the breed which followed Diana in the chase, and a javelin which could not miss a mark at which it might be aimed.

These were valuable presents for a hunter, and day by day they brought good fortune to Cephalus, and he returned laden always with spoil. The dog was so fleet of foot, and so tireless, that no quarry could hope to outrun him, and his prowess at length attracted the notice of the gods, who determined to put his qualities to a difficult test. They set in his path one day a fox which they had specially created for the purpose, and, true to his breed, the dog immediately started upon a chase, which lasted for many a long hour. Up hill and down dale raced the flying animals, and so well were they matched that there seemed nothing to choose between their speed and endurance. How long they would have raced on I cannot say, but the gods at length took pity on them, and in gratitude for the fine sport, and in admiration of the spirited animals, they changed them into statues, so true to life that no human hand could have carved the like.

Each evening when the sun was nearing the grey shades which rose to receive him over the distant line of hills, the hunter would return to his comfortable home and the loving welcome which awaited him. There seemed to be no cloud over the humble dwelling, and perhaps the happy Cephalus could not spare a thought for the divine lady who had sought his love. But, as you know, the gods could be very cruel in their jealousy, and Aurora was waiting for an opportunity to cut short this dream of wedded bliss.

In the summer days, when the heat was so oppressive that not even the wild bee's hum disturbed the heavy silence, Cephalus would cast himself down at times in the long grass under the shade of some tree, and he would playfully call upon the passing zephyrs to cool his heated brow. This became a habit, and his voice might often be heard at noon from the leafy grove where most he loved to recline, " Sweet air, oh, come ! " while the voice of Echo would reply, " Come, sweet air ! "

Now Aurora knew of this habit, and although she knew also that the hunter spoke only to the passing breeze, she resolved to turn it to her own ends. She therefore went to Procris and informed her that at noon each day her faithless husband sported with some forest nymph in the recesses of a distant wood. The poor wife fell an easy victim to the wiles of the goddess. Without losing a moment she hastened to the grove where she guessed her husband would be found, disregarding the noontide rays which beat in full force upon her head. Concealing her slight figure in the undergrowth which abounded, she waited and listened, all breathless with the emotions which surged with savage force through her usually gentle soul.

Soon she saw the careless figure of the hunter making for the very covert in which she lay, and throwing himself upon the ground at its edge she heard him cry, " Sweet air, oh, come ! "

Her worst fears were realized, and weakened by her emotion, and by the long journey in the midday heat, she fell back swooning upon the ground.

The noise, as of some forest creature stealing through the covert, aroused the instinct of the hunter. Forgetting his weariness, he started to his feet, and, poising the fatal javelin, he sent it with unerring aim into the midst of the tangled growth. The next moment he realized his error. The weapon had pierced his faithful wife's bosom, and there could be no mistaking that piteous moan. With an affrighted bound he was by her side in an instant, and quickly raising her dying head he saw that few indeed were her remaining moments. Many words were impossible, but in that supreme moment the pitying gods permitted Cephalus to learn the reason of his wife's presence, and ere she breathed her last in his arms she knew that her husband had not been false to her, and, caring for naught else, her soul departed joyously to the shades.

The God of Fire

THE god Vulcan was in many ways different from the other deities of Olympus. He dwelt usually in the forest solitudes of Mount Ætna and rarely joined the gods when they assembled in council. He loved to engage in toil as though he were an ordinary inhabitant of earth, and in partnership with the Cyclopes he set up a forge in the interior of the mountain, and here, with his assistants, he manufactured all sorts of wonderful objects.

He was known by a limp, which he had contracted in this way. Having interfered in a quarrel between Jupiter and Juno the enraged god hurled him out of his presence, and the young deity fell to earth like a meteor. His fall lasted for a day and a night, and he landed at last upon the Island of Lemnos with such a shock, that only a god could have survived it. Even Vulcan did not escape uninjured, and for ever after he walked with a limp.

The goddess Juno did not much concern herself for the fate of her son, and in fact she did not try to find out whether he had lived or died. This lack of affection and gratitude greatly affected Vulcan, and it was the principal cause of his preference for his own mountain retreat.

Many cunning works did Vulcan devise, and among the number was a throne of gold with hidden springs so arranged that the arms would contract and hold fast anyone who ventured to sit upon it. This was intended for Juno, and, when completed, Vulcan dispatched it to the queen-goddess, who received it with delight. No sooner, however, had she taken her seat upon it than the treacherous arms closed round her, and she found herself a safe prisoner. In vain the gods came to her assistance. Their strength and skill would not avail against the cunning workmanship of Vulcan, and there was nothing for it but to find some means to induce him to relent.

So Mercury was sent with a soothing message, and a flattering invitation that he should visit Olympus, but Vulcan well knew the reason for this sudden desire for his company, and all the eloquence of Mercury could not avail to move him from his forge.

Then the gods decided to send Bacchus as ambassador in the hope that he could move the heart of Vulcan.

The god of wine proceeded upon the mission in quite a different way. He did not trust to the power of argument, but selecting his choicest vintage he appeared to Vulcan just at the moment when, wearied with his toil, he was most in need of refreshment, and after a courteous salutation he offered a cup of wine. Almost without a thought Vulcan accepted the proffered gift, and he drained the cup again and again.

Now was the moment for argument, and very soon Vulcan had yielded himself to his visitor's persuasions and was on the way to the court of Heaven. Arrived there he liberated Juno, and became reconciled to his father and mother.

Although he would not dwell always upon Olympus he remained upon friendly terms with his brother gods, and many were the wonderful works which he wrought for them in the heart of Mount Ætna. Amongst the marvellous gifts which he made to mortals who were favoured with his friendship, were the fire-breathing bulls afterwards slain by Jason in the land of Colchis, and the wonderful suit of armour worn by the hero Achilles. To this day fire and smoke may be seen ascending to the blue sky whenever some mighty work is in progress upon the giant forge.

A Faithless King

AGES before the famous battles waged between the Greeks and the Trojans for the possession of the city of Troy, there was a king in that city, named Laomedon.

It was in his reign that the massive walls were raised which so long defied the assaults of the Greeks, and well might they stand securely, for they were built by Neptune and Apollo.

The Sea God had been banished to Earth by Jupiter because he suspected that Neptune intended to obtain powers that belonged to himself, and the jealous monarch of Olympus included in his rival's punishment a term of service with some earthly king.

Thus it happened that Neptune undertook to raise the walls of Troy, and Apollo lightened his tedious labours the while with delightful strains from his lyre. He, too, was at that time in banishment from the court of Jupiter, and fellow-feeling makes gods as well as men wondrous kind.

Now Laomedon had been very glad to obtain the help of Neptune, and he had willingly undertaken to pay him generously. He was a mean and crafty man, however, and when the task had been performed and the goodly walls stood securely on all sides, he refused to carry out his part of the bargain and sent Neptune away with empty hands.

In this he acted not only dishonestly but very foolishly, as he might have expected that so powerful an ally could find means to punish his heartless breach of faith.

Punishment was not long, indeed, in coming, and Laomedon soon received tidings that every day a great serpent came out of the depths of Ocean and, going up and down the land, devoured the children of his people.

All attempts to kill this terrible beast failed miserably, and many a brave man met a cruel death in his endeavour to save some loved little one.

At length the Trojans asked counsel of their favourite oracle, and the dread reply came forth : "Not otherwise canst thou free thy land but by the sacrifice of a beautiful maiden."

Alas ! there was no other way, and lots being cast, the dreaded fate fell upon a young and lovely girl, who was led by the priests to the seashore and chained to a slippery rock at the edge of the tide. Before long the monster made his accustomed appearance, and having devoured his victim he

returned to the wave, and for a whole year the
country was free from his ravages.

But when the king and his people had begun
to forget the terrible scourge which had ranged
their country twelve months since, once more
the dreaded monster issued from the sea, and
again it was found necessary to purchase safety
by the sacrifice of a daughter of the land.

Year after year the horrible creature reappeared
to take toll of the suffering Trojans, and in due
time it came to pass that the lot fell upon the
Princess Hesione, only daughter of King Laomedon.

Then was the king crushed to earth by the
terrible fate which threatened his beloved child,
and he made the most frantic efforts to save her.

But even the king was powerless to protect his
daughter when once the sacred lot had fallen upon
her. His only hope was to find a champion who
would dare to attack the monster, and he hastened
to send heralds throughout the neighbouring
countries, offering rich rewards to him who should
rid the land of its dreaded foe.

Now it happened that Hercules heard the pro-
clamation of one of the king's heralds, and he immediately proceeded to Troy.

In the meantime the fatal day had arrived, and
a mournful procession had escorted the wretched
princess to the seashore, where, in her turn, she

was fastened to the rock from which the serpent had snatched so many other beautiful maidens of her land. The priests had withdrawn, and the miserable father was dragging himself from the awful sight which was momentarily expected when, hot with haste, the hero Hercules appeared.

He had barely time to bid the king take heart, when, with the noise of a thousand waves breaking upon a rock-bound shore, the foul monster issued from the deep and advanced to seize his prey. Ere he could reach the rock, however, Hercules had bounded to the spot, and with rapid blows of his terrible club he crushed its head, and the brute serpent lay a mass of nerveless coils at the hero's feet.

Great was the joy of Laomedon, and Hesione knelt in her gratitude to her deliverer, while the assembled Trojans rent the air with their applause. Well might they shout at the deed which had delivered them that day from the nightmare that had poisoned their waking hours for so many years.

One would think that the story should be ended here, but, true to his nature, once more Laomedon broke faith and denied the reward which he had publicly promised to whoever should deliver his daughter and the land.

Hercules strode from the royal presence in contempt of the man who could thus go back upon his

plighted word, and he took the first opportunity
of gathering a band of heroes, with whom he sailed
in six galleys for Troy, and forcing his way into the
city he seized the royal palace and put the king
and queen to death.

As for Hesione, she was carried away captive to
the land of Greece, and in that fair country she
became the bride of Telamon, the friend and companion of Hercules.

THE winds that once the Argo bore
   Have died by Neptune's ruined shrines,
And her hull is the drift of the deep sea-floor,
Though shaped of Pelion's tallest pines.
You may seek her crew on every isle
Fair in the foam of Ægean seas,
But, out of their rest, no charm can wile
Jason and Orpheus and Hercules.

Mother Earth! Are the heroes dead?
Do they thrill the soul of the years no more?
Are the gleaming snows and the poppies red
All that is left of the brave of yore?
Are there none to fight as Theseus fought?
Far in the young world's mist dawn?
Or to teach as the grey-haired Nestor taught?
Mother Earth! are the heroes gone?

Gone? In a grander form they rise;
Dead? We may clasp their hands in ours;
And catch the light of their clearer eyes,
And wreathe their brows with immortal flowers.
Wherever a noble deed is done
'Tis the pulse of a hero's heart is stirred;
Wherever Right has a triumph won
There are the heroes' voices heard.

Their armour rings on a fairer field
Than the Greek and the Trojan fiercely trod;
For Freedom's sword is the blade they wield,
And the light above is the smile of God.
So, in his isle of calm delight,
Jason may sleep the years away;
For the heroes live and the sky is bright,
And the world is a braver world to-day.

E. D. PROCTOR

PRONOUNCING LIST OF NAMES

Ă-chĭl′lēs (kil).
Ā′çis.
Ac-tae′on.
Ae′gē-an.
Ae′geus (jūs).
Ae′son.
Aet′na.
An-drŏm′e-da.
A-pŏl′lo.
A-rä∈h′nè.
Ăr′∈as.
Ăr′go.
Ăr′go-nauts.
Ăr′gos.
Ăr′gus.
A-ri-ăd′ne.
Ăth′ens.
Au-rō′ra.

Băc′chŭs (kus).
Bau′çìs.

Cal-lĭs′to.
Cas-si-o-pē′ia.
Çĕn′taur.
Çĕph′ă-lus.
Çē′rēs.
Çē′ўx.
∈hä′ron.
∈hĭ′ron.
∈ïr′çē.
Cŏl′∈his.
Crēte.
Cu′pid.
Çȳ′clops.
Çȳclo′pēs.
Çyn′thia.
Çȳp-a-rĭs′sus.
Çȳ′prus.

Dae′da-lus.

Dăn′ă-ē.
Dăph′ne.
Dĕ-ī-a-nī′-ra.
Di-án′a.

E∈h′o.
Ē′gўpt.
Epi-mē′theūs.
Eū-rўd′i-çē.

Găl-a-tē′a.
Glau′∈us.
Grēēçe.
Gôr′gons.

Hä′dēṣ.
Hăl-cȳ′o-nē.
Hĕl′lē.
Her′cū-lēs.
Hē-sĭ′ō-nē.
Hes′pe-rŭs.
Hȳ-a-cĭn′thus.

Ĭ-∈ā′ri-an.
I∈′a-rus.
I′no.
I′o.
I′ris.
I′sis.

Jā′son.
Jū′no.
Jū′pi-ter.

Lä-ŏm′ĕ-dŏn.
La-tō′na.

Mar′sȳ-as.
Me-dē′a.
Mĕd-i-ter-rā′ne-an.
Me-dū′sa.
Mĕr′eū-ry.

Mī′das.
Mĭ-ner′va.
Mī′nos.
Mĭn′o-taur.

Nar-çĭs′sus.
Nĕph′e-lē.
Nĕp′tune.
Nĕs′sus.
Nĕs′tor.
Nīle.
Nĭ′o-bē.

O-lўm′pus.
Ôr′pheūs.

Păn.
Păn′dō-ră.
Pē′li-ŏn.
Pĕr′dix.
Pĕr′seus.
Phi-lē′mon.
Phrўx′us.
Plū′to.
Pŏl-y-phē′mus.
Prō′cris.
Pro-ser′pine.
Pўg-mä′li-on.

Sçўl′la (sĭl).
Sĭç′i-ly.
Sŏm′nus.
Sȳ′rĭṇx.

Thēbes.
Thē′seūs.
Trō′jan.
Troy.

Vē′nus.
Vul′can.

221